For H

✧ ✧ ✧

The American Singer

✧ ✧ BOOK ONE ✧ ✧

John W. Beattie

DEAN, THE SCHOOL OF MUSIC, NORTHWESTERN UNIVERSITY
EVANSTON, ILLINOIS

Josephine Wolverton

ASSISTANT SUPERVISOR, EVANSTON SCHOOLS
ASSISTANT PROFESSOR, THE SCHOOL OF MUSIC, NORTHWESTERN UNIVERSITY
EVANSTON, ILLINOIS

Grace V. Wilson

DIRECTOR OF MUSIC, PUBLIC SCHOOLS, WICHITA, KANSAS

Howard Hinga

ASSISTANT DIRECTOR OF MUSIC, PUBLIC SCHOOLS
INSTRUCTOR OF PUBLIC SCHOOL MUSIC, EASTMAN SCHOOL OF MUSIC
ROCHESTER, NEW YORK

✧ ✧ ✧

American Book Company

NEW YORK   CINCINNATI   CHICAGO
BOSTON   ATLANTA   DALLAS   SAN FRANCISCO

Acknowledgments

For their help in preparing this book, grateful acknowledgment is made to the following:

Elizabeth Waterman, Teacher of Physical Education, Chicago Public Schools, for her contribution to the rhythm program.

Mayme Christenson, Opal Dillon, Jane Hebblethwaite, Iva Sleer and their classes of children in the Evanston schools for their assistance in evaluating material.

Theodore Lams, Ewald Nolte, and Ella Rose Wright for harmonizations and accompaniments.

Dr. and Mrs. Charles Seeger for research into American folk literature.

Child Training Association for "A Song to Mother" by Gertrude Bartlett Kellman from *Children's Activities Magazine*.

E. P. Dutton & Company, Inc. for the selection from *Now We Are Six* by A. A. Milne.

Henry Holt & Company, Inc. for the stanza from *Many, Many Moons* by Lew Sarett.

Robert M. McBride & Company for the stanza from *The Coffee Pot Face* by Aileen Fisher.

Rand McNally & Company for the selection from *Peter Patter Book* by LeRoy Jackson.

Beattie and others, The American Singer, Book One

E. P. 8

Made in U. S. A.

Rote Singing

Two types of songs are presented in this book for the children's initial experience in music. They are:

1. The melodic rote song, identified by its smooth, flowing melody, such as is found in a lullaby

2. The rhythmic rote song, identified by its definite rhythmic pattern, such as is found in "Hey Jim Along," p. 152.

The Melodic Rote Song

1. ITS USE

Children should be given the opportunity for musical expression in various moods, just as they have variety of mood in reading experiences. Too often it has been thought that children respond only to gay and rollicking tunes and that they are too immature to express themselves in the more thoughtful and quiet moods.

In this highly complex life in which he lives, the child should often be given lovely, expressive melodies to quiet and soothe him. His first introduction to music was through the lullabies sung to him by his mother, and he will enjoy such songs throughout his life. Every music lesson should contain songs which stimulate and others which quiet him. For the latter the melodic rote song is used.

2. TEMPO AND MOOD

The tempo or rate of speed and degrees of loudness or softness vary according to the mood of the song. Such variations will be apparent in the songs listed below:

Rockaby, Baby, p. 12.
The Child and the Star, p. 5.
The Oriole, p. 54.
The North Wind, p. 38.
Autumn, p. 32.
Night Time, p. 104.

The text may be suggestive of the mood, although the key to interpretation is often found in the melody alone.

3. PHRASING AND INTERPRETATION

The phrases of a melodic rote song are usually longer than those of a rhythmic rote song. This does not imply that there are more notes and measures required for the melodic phrase, but rather that more time is required in singing it. Regardless of the time required in singing the phrase, it should be sung with one breath.

The teacher will have little difficulty in obtaining a smooth phrase if she appeals to the imagination of the child to tell the story of the song as it should be told, without breaking the flow of the melody.

Good phrasing in singing may be compared to that which the violinist produces when he uses long bowing strokes on the strings of his violin. In the discussion of rhythm on p. 109 are listed devices which will be helpful in securing good phrasing:

a. In singing games, a suggested movement for each phrase

b. Turning on a phrase

c. Rising and bending, each movement on a phrase

The Rhythmic Rote Song

1. ITS USE

Rhythmic rote songs are bright and gay in character and are used to develop the feeling for rhythm through accentuation of pulse and rhythmic beat. Some of the songs contain rhythm patterns for walking, running, skipping, swaying, jumping, rowing, stretching, and bending. A more detailed study of these rhythms will be found under the chapter heading RHYTHM.

2. ENUNCIATION

All songs should be sung with clear enunciation, especially rhythmic rote songs. In order that each tone may have proper value, free lip movement is essential, with special attention paid to the consonants, which often accentuate the rhythm. This type of singing is best illustrated by the violinist who uses short, staccato bowing for each tone produced. It might be compared, also, to the trumpeter who tongues each note separately rather than slurs tones together without breaks. Songs of this type must be sung with sprightly bouncing rhythm. Many rhythmic rote songs require action to bring out their musical qualities, but others do not. Examples of these types are found under RHYTHM. Other examples are:

It's Raining, p. 44.
Three Little Kittens, p. 78.
Squirrel Has a Bushy Tail, p. 78.

Teaching the Rote Song

1. THE TEACHER'S VOICE QUALITY

The teacher's own voice quality influences that of the children. If she sings in a loud, raucous voice, the tone of the children will also be very unmusical. Her tones should be light and childlike, and should approximate the quality of the children's voices. If she has a limited range and cannot sing very high, she should pitch the song in a key comfortable for her when she sings the song to the children. However, when she teaches the song to the children, it should be pitched in the key in which it is written and which is appropriate for children's voices.

2. THE CHILDREN'S VOICE QUALITY

Children at this age have two vocal registers. One is the chest voice, characterized by a harsh, reedy, unpleasant sound. The other is the head voice, characterized by a light, thin, unforced flutelike quality. Children should sing with this head voice at all times. Singing with a light tone will insure carrying the head voice downward through the entire scale. The teacher should, however, guard against such expressions as "Sing softly" or "Sing with tiny voices." They are apt to result in a breathy devitalized type of singing which is not a natural childlike expression. Good tone quality is to a great degree based upon imagination, spontaneity, and light singing.

3. PITCH

The teacher should depend on the pitch pipe for the key note and not on her own sense of pitch, which in most cases is inaccurate, usually too low. If there are several verses in a song, it may be necessary to refer to the pitch pipe between the verses. Sometimes there is a tendency to flat on wide skips; the top note is just under the pitch. The teacher may anticipate this difficulty by occasionally saying, "Think high" or "Make it wider." Singing that is spontaneous, strongly rhythmic, and of light quality will seldom be off pitch.

4. CONDUCTING

It is necessary for the teacher to indicate the rhythmic flow of the music. She can do this most effectively by beating the time with a small, graceful gesture. The teacher who stands before the class in a stolid, uncommunicative manner will not stimulate children to sing in a rhythmic and expressive manner. The personality of the teacher—her enthusiasm, facial expression, and spontaneity have much to do with artistic singing. Effective and appropriate conducting is one of the most tangible means of communicating musical feeling to the children.

5. ENUNCIATION

The words of the song should be clearly enunciated. Sometimes children substitute words that are familiar but completely foreign to the text of the song itself. Unfamiliar words should be explained and pronounced to the child. The vowel sounds should be pure, and the initial and final consonants should be clearly articulated. There should be no difficulty on the part of the children in repeating the phrase correctly if the teacher is careful about her own enunciation.

6. INTERPRETATION

The teacher should teach the song in the mood and the tempo in which the song was intended to be sung. Variations in speed or degree of loudness indicated by the expression marks should be taught with the first presentation and not after the song has been sung many times.

7. USE OF THE PIANO

Most songs should be taught without the piano. When the song is well learned, the accompaniment may be added. The art of accompanying applies to children as it does to adults. The accompaniment should be soft enough to allow the children's voices to predominate. Furthermore, the piano influences the quantity of tone which they use. If the accompaniment is loud, the children will shout above it. Little or no pedal should be used. It blurs the voices and covers up the lovely quality of children's voices. Accompaniments in this manual are simple, yet effective, and should add much to the full enjoyment of the songs. It should be noted, however, that many songs are intended for unaccompanied singing and will actually sound better without the accompaniment.

Procedure for Teaching a Rote Song

SONGS TAUGHT WITHOUT BOOKS

a. The teacher sings the song two or three days in advance of teaching it to the children. She thereby not only enables them to enjoy it and builds up a desire to learn it but gives them an opportunity to hear the song as a whole.

b. When the song is to be taught, the teacher sings it through to the children. She may follow it by comments on the words and a discussion of the meaning of the song.

c. If the song is short and not difficult, the teacher may ask the class to sing the whole song with her. (The repeated hearing of the song enables them to do so.)

d. The teacher re-sings phrases or measures in which errors occur and has the children repeat them after her.

e. If the song is long and more difficult, the teacher sings each phrase and has the class repeat it after her. The teacher then sings the entire song and has the class repeat it. (If difficulties still persist, the same procedure may have to be repeated another time.)

Out-of-tune Singing

1. BACKGROUND

Children enter school with widely different musical backgrounds. Some come from homes in which there has been singing or instrumental music. In some cases parents have taught children to sing simple songs. Others come from homes in which there has been no music at all, and the child has in no way been encouraged to express himself through music. These children may find singing an entirely new experience.

2. POSSIBLE CAUSES

a. Physical handicaps

The ability to sing is influenced by physical conditions. The speaking voice may be hoarse or low in pitch due to enlarged tonsils, malnutrition, nervous disorders, or other physical difficulties.

b. Lack of musical background

Children who have had no musical background may find difficulty in singing in the first few months of school.

c. Lack of co-ordination

A child may hear the tone correctly but fail to produce the right pitch. This failure may be due to his inability to co-ordinate ear and voice.

Grouping

In music as in other subjects, the teacher must recognize various levels of ability. In teaching the children to read, the teacher gives considerable attention to the individual child. There may be several reading groups in one room, depending upon the varying degrees of ability. It is possible under such conditions to meet the needs of the individual children.

In music it is also necessary to provide musical experiences which meet individual needs. Children should be grouped according to their varying abilities to sing. It may be desirable to divide the class into three or four different groups, in order that the teacher may work more efficiently within the short music period.

GROUP 1

Children in this group can sing the song correctly alone and with the group. They should be seated in a row at the back of the class, so that their voices will aid and strengthen the entire group.

GROUP 2

Children in this group may be able to sing the song correctly with Group 1, but can sing only short phrases of the song alone. These children should be seated immediately in front of Group 1.

GROUP 3

a. Some children in this group can sing only short motives (a small group of tones) from a simple song; they cannot carry a complete phrase.

b. Other children in this group cannot match a single tone. All the children in Group 3 should be seated at the front of the class. If the teacher so desires, the children who do not match single pitches may be seated directly in front, making a fourth group.

Specific Aids

It is beneficial for the entire class to sing together at different times during the music lesson. However, group singing should not constitute the entire singing experience. In each lesson it is necessary to meet the singing needs of the smaller groups within the class, and the needs of the individual pupil.

GROUP 2

Each child individually and with the group should sing short phrases taken from the song previously learned by Group 1. This experience will gradually give the child the ability to sing the entire song alone and with the group.

GROUP 3

a. Each child should be given continued experience in singing short motives (two or three tones) from a simple song previously learned by Group 1. These children will gradually be able to sing an entire phrase.

b. Each child should have continued experience in matching single tones sung by the teacher.

1. LOW-PITCH SINGERS

a. Have these children imitate a siren beginning on a low pitch and ascending to a high tone.

b. Begin on the pitch which the child sounds and imitate a whistle (too-too). When this is correctly sung, work upward stepwise.

2. HIGH-PITCH SINGERS

a. These children may imitate a siren beginning on a high pitch and descending to a low tone.

b. Begin on the pitch which the child sounds and imitate a whistle (too-too). When this is correctly sung, work downward stepwise.

3. OTHER DEVICES

a. When children can match single tones, use two different pitches (do-la) on a bird call (cuckoo). Also use ringing bells (ding-dong).

b. Use calls employing the names of children. The teacher or a child from Group 1 may call "Mary." Another child may answer on the same pitch, "I'm here." This may be varied by imitating the huckster selling fruits or vegetables.

HOME
Lullaby

Adapted

Breton Folk Song

dear lit - tle broth - er;   Do   not cry,   dear   broth - er   of   mine.
        (sis - ter)   (sis - ter)

The Child and the Star

Slowly and smoothly

J. W. Elliott

1. Lit - tle   star that shines   so bright,   Come and   peep   at   me to - night;
2. Lit - tle   child,   at   you   I   peep,   While you   lie   so   fast a - sleep;

For   I   oft - en   watch for you   In   the   pret - ty   sky   so blue.
But when   morn be - gins   to break,   I   my   home - ward   jour - ney take.

Calling

J. W. Beattie

J. W. Beattie

1. Hel - lo, hel - lo, hel - lo!—— Come o - ver and join in our play.——
2. Oh no, oh no, oh no!—— I have to help Moth - er to - day.——

Dolly's Lullaby

Ruth Wilson Kelsey

Grace V. Wilson

Go to sleep, my doll - y, Close your pret - ty eyes,——

Soon you will be sleep - ing, Lull - a - lull - a - by.——

Sleepy Time

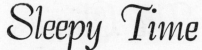

H. Hinga

French Folk Song

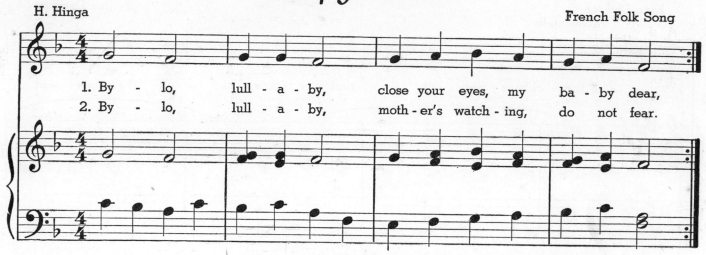

1. By - lo, lull - a - by, close your eyes, my ba - by dear,
2. By - lo, lull - a - by, moth - er's watch - ing, do not fear.

Baby's Song

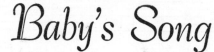

Lilith Rushing

Grace V. Wilson

1. Tin - kle, tin - kle, tin - kle, Tin - kle, tin - kle tee,
2. With his bus - y fin - gers, With his dish and spoon,

Ba - by in his high chair Makes a song for me.
Tin - kle, tin - kle, tin - kle Makes a hap - py tune.

The Chimes

Nina Dawson

Moderately

Nina Dawson

The chimes ring out a pret-ty tune, They tell the time of day; "Do ti la sol fa mi re do," Their mu-sic seems to say.

Accompany the song by triangles or chimes.

Sugar John

Old Song sung in Georgia

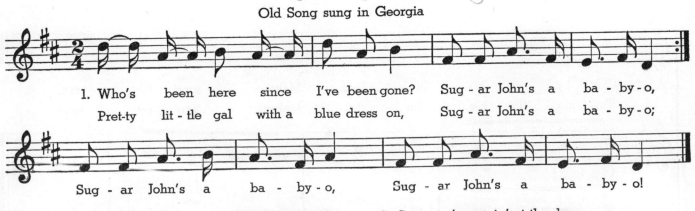

1. Who's been here since I've been gone? Sug-ar John's a ba-by-o,
Pret-ty lit-tle gal with a blue dress on, Sug-ar John's a ba-by-o;
Sug-ar John's a ba-by-o, Sug-ar John's a ba-by-o!

2. Who's that comin' down the street?
Silver slippers on her feet.

3. Someone's rappin' at the door,
Been here many times before.

(8)

My Little Red Wagon

J. W. Beattie

J. W. Beattie

1. My lit - tle red wag - on is lots of fun, It runs as well as a Ford;— A - long on the side - walk we roll and run, Look out for us, all a - board!

2. My little red wagon is lots of fun, The best of all of my toys;—
   Along on the sidewalk we roll and run, All loaded with girls and boys.
   Accompany the song by triangle rolls (see Instruments, page 157).

The Telephone

W. Bates

W. Bates

1. Ting - a - ling - a - ling! Hear the tel - e - phone bell ring!
2. Ting - a - ling - a - ling! Hear the tel - e - phone bell ring!

If Moth - er can - not an - swer, I like to go.
I take down the re - ceiv - er and say, "Hel - lo!"

Accompany the song by triangle rolls.

Washing Dishes

Martha Wonn

Martha Wonn

My dad-dy made a lit-tle stool, so I could stand up high

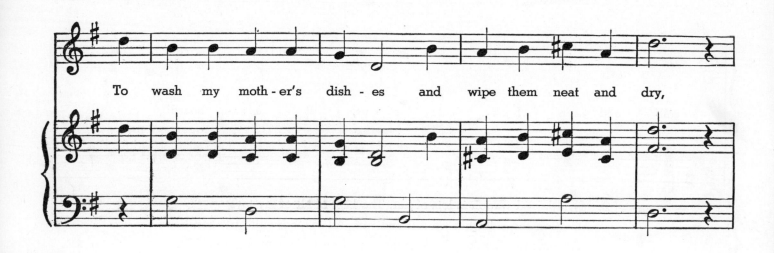

To wash my moth-er's dish-es and wipe them neat and dry,

Plate and cup and sau - cer, knife and fork and spoon,

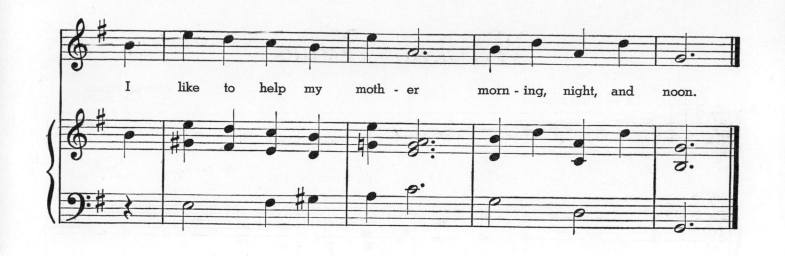

I like to help my moth - er morn - ing, night, and noon.

A Song to Mother

Gertrude Bartlett Kellman

Gertrude Bartlett Kellman

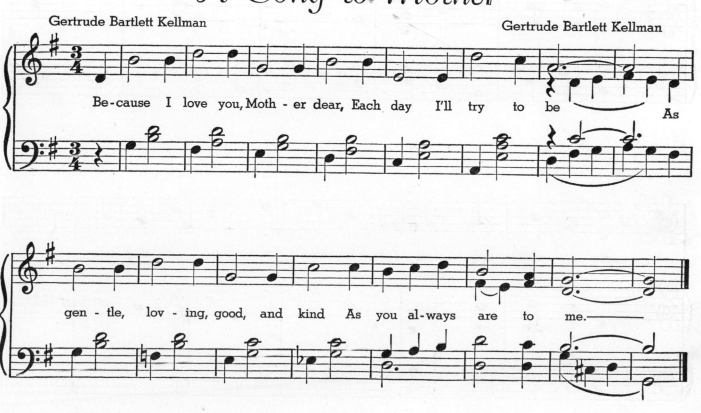

Be-cause I love you, Moth - er dear, Each day I'll try to be As

gen - tle, lov - ing, good, and kind As you al - ways are to me.

Rockaby, Baby

Quietly, with swaying rhythm

Old Song

Rock - a - by, ba - by, on the tree - top, When the wind

blows, the cra - dle will rock; When the bough breaks, the

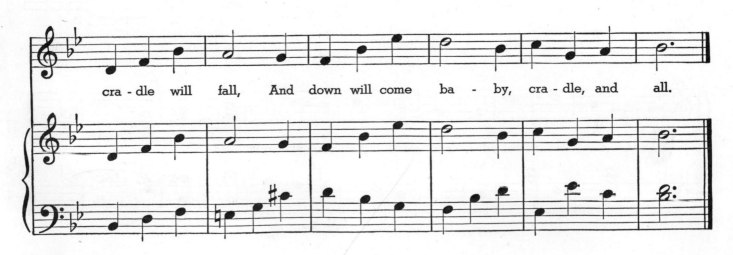

cra - dle will fall, And down will come ba - by, cra - dle, and all.

SCHOOL

In School

Mayme Christenson

Alma Spear

Not fast, smoothly

We sit in the cir - cle and talk to - geth - er, And talk to - geth - er

And talk to - geth - er, We sit in the cir - cle and talk to - geth - er,

That's what I like a - bout school.——

Other suggestions: Sing together.   Read together.   Tell our stories.

Days of the Week

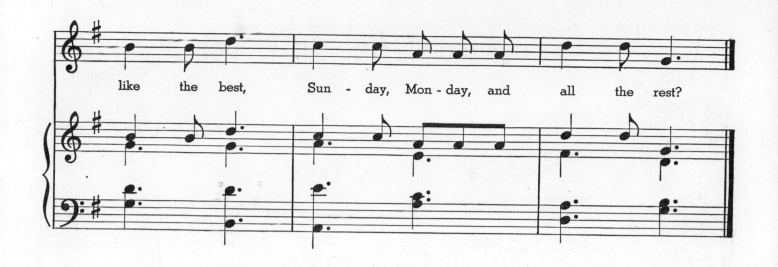

like the best, Sun - day, Mon - day, and all the rest?

School Time

Mayme Christenson

Russel Godfrey

Ding, dong, ding, dong! Hear the school bell ring - ing,

Ding, dong, ding, dong! Play - time now is done.

Accompany the song by triangles.

Working Time Is Over

Jean Hoover

J. Rinck

Working time is over, Things are put a - way,

We will leave our les - sons For an - oth - er day.

A Birthday Song

William Dennis

William Dennis

This is (Sal - ly's) birth - day, birth - day, birth - day;

This is (Sal - ly's) birth - day, We'll count the years a - - way.

After the children have sung the song, they chant 1, 2, 3, 4, 5 or 1, 2, 3, 4, 5, 6—the birthday count. Then they repeat the song.

The Slide
(Scale Song)

Lea Young

Lea Young

We climb up the lad - der and shoot down the slide,

We're tak - ing a fast and a fu - ri - ous ride.

Good Morning

Good morn - ing, good morn - ing, Good morn - ing to you!

Good morn - ing, good morn - ing! Oh, how do you do?

Morning Song

1. Bless - ed Lord of night and morn - ing,
2. Work - ing, play - ing, may we please —— Thee,

Keep us safe from— harm this day.
Kind in all we— do and say.

OCCUPATIONS
The Scissors Grinder's Bell

Russel Godfrey   Russel Godfrey

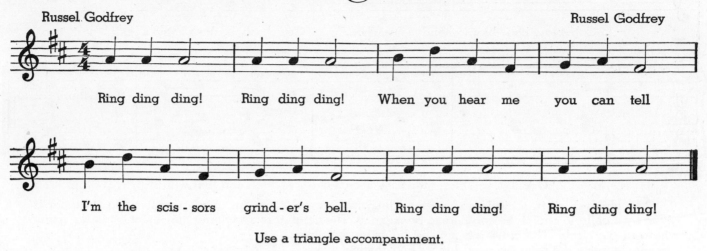

Ring ding ding! Ring ding ding! When you hear me you can tell

I'm the scis-sors grind-er's bell. Ring ding ding! Ring ding ding!

Use a triangle accompaniment.

The Traffic Man

J. W. Beattie   J. W. Beattie

1. Old Pat Mo-ran is a traf-fic man,
2. Says Pat Mo-ran, "Help me all you can,

He helps all the chil-dren cross the street.
Look out when you go a-cross the street!"

Formation: "Pat Moran" stands in the center of an imaginary intersection. The children divide into four groups, and each group stands at one of the four approaches to the intersection. As the officer motions for north and south traffic, the north and south groups change places. The east and west groups change places, likewise, when their signal is given.

Cobbler

English Folk Song

1. Cob-bler, cob-ler, mend my shoe, Get it done by half past two.

2. Cobbler, cobbler, mend my shoe, Give it a stitch and that will do.

The children sit in a circle and pretend that they are cobblers. An object representing a slipper is given by a child to one of the cobblers to be mended. The child goes away, and the object is hidden somewhere in the circle. The child returns and hunts for the object.

Accompany the song by wood blocks and rhythm sticks.

Mister Baker

J. W. Beattie

J. W. Beattie

Brightly
Child:

1. Good morn-ing, Mis-ter Bak-er-man, What have you made to-day?
2. Oh, thank you, Mis-ter Bak-er-man, That's ver-y nice of you.

Baker:

For you a nice big cook-ie-man With seeds of car-a-way.
Now take this pack-age home with you, There're cakes for Moth-er too.

The Vegetable Man

George Kent

Old Tune

Buy my ripe corn and to - ma - toes!

Try a nice ap - ple or pear! I have fresh beans and po-

ta - toes; Best you can find an - y - where!

The Fire Department

George Kent
Fast

George Kent

Cling, cling, cling! Here comes the truck and en - gine.

Cling, cling, cling! They're com - ing up the street.

Use triangles, gongs, and cymbals to accompany the first and third phrases.

Shopping

J. Wolverton

J. Wolverton

Child:

1. Mis - ter Gro - cer, tell me, please, what do you have to - day?——

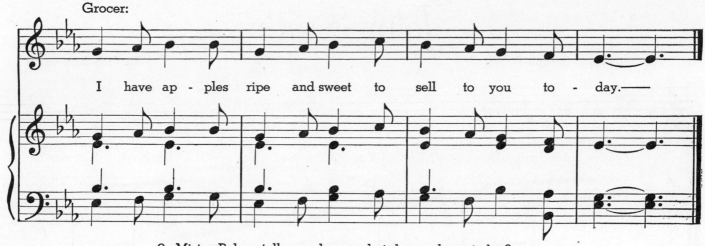

Grocer:

I have ap - ples ripe and sweet to sell to you to - day.——

2. Mister Baker, tell me, please, what do you have today?
   I have cookies crisp and brown to sell to you today.

3. Mister Milkman, tell me, please, what do you have today?
   I have butter, eggs, and milk to sell to you today.

The Postman

George Kent   George Kent

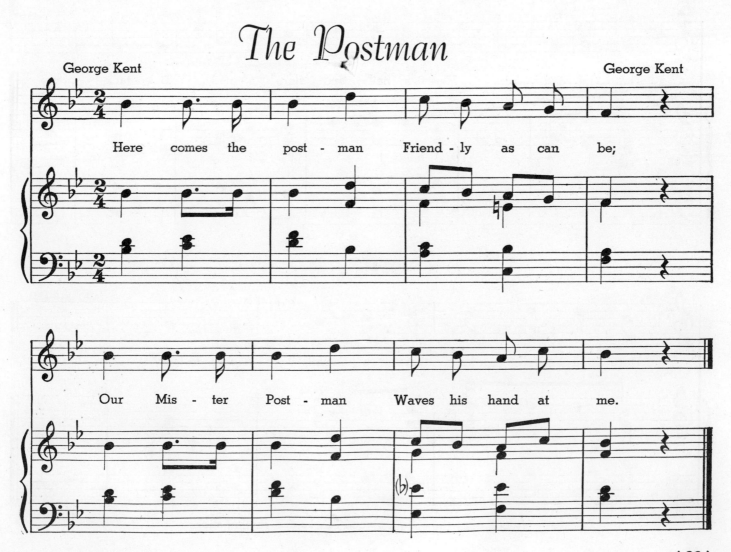

Here comes the post - man Friend - ly as can be;

Our Mis - ter Post - man Waves his hand at me.

(23)

John Smith

Mother Goose (adapted)

English Folk Tune
(adapted)

Does John Smith live here? Yes, that is he; Can he make a shoe?

That he can do; Here a nail and there a nail, Tick, tack, too;

Here a nail and there a nail, Tick, tack, too.

Accompany the song by wood blocks and rhythm sticks.

(24)

TRAVEL
Be Careful

Stop, look, lis - ten be - fore you cross the street.

Crossing the Street

J. Wolverton

Opal Dillon

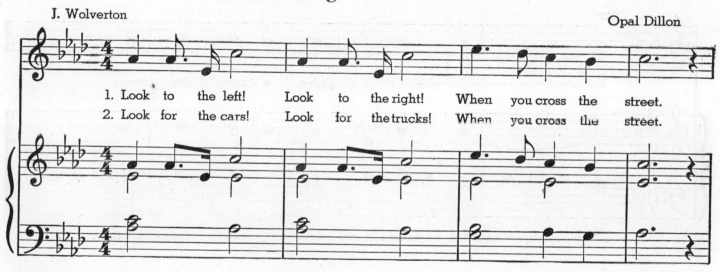

1. Look to the left! Look to the right! When you cross the street.
2. Look for the cars! Look for the trucks! When you cross the street.

Look to the left! Look to the right! When you cross the street.
Look for the cars! Look for the trucks! When you cross the street.

My Airplane

Zoom————— oh, see my plane a-fly-ing!

Zoom————— It glides a-bove the trees.

As an accompaniment use a cymbal roll and a drum roll, using two sticks alternately.

Conductor's Call

All a-board! all a-board! This train stops at Al-ba-ny,

Syr-a-cuse, Roch-es-ter, Buf-fa-lo. All a-board!

Let the children use the names of any familiar towns or cities.

Transportation

J. W. Beattie

Variant on an old tune

Fast

1. The train is com-ing down the track: Choo-choo-choo-choo-choo choo!—

It goes to Ev-ans-ville and back: Choo-choo-choo-choo-choo-choo!—

2. The boat is coming down the lake,
   Whoo-oo-whoo-oo-whoo-oo!
   A landing here it has to make,
   Whoo-oo-whoo-oo-whoo-oo!

3. The bus is coming down the road,
   Toot-oo-toot-oo-toot-oo!
   It always hauls a heavy load,
   Toot-oo-toot-oo-toot-oo!

4. The airplane circles in the sky,
   Zoo-zoo-zoo-zoo-zoo-zoo!
   I like to stand and watch it fly,
   Zoo-zoo-zoo-zoo-zoo-zoo!

(27)

Wait for the Wagon

Adapted

Old Song

It's ear-ly in the morn-ing, And I am by your side;

We'll jump in-to the wag-on And we'll all take a ride.

Wait for the wag-on, Wait for the wag-on,

Wait for the wag-on and we'll all take a ride.

The Freight Train

J. W. Beattie

J. W. Beattie

Fast

Click - e - ty, click - e - ty, clack, clack, clack, The

freight train is com - ing a - long the track; It rum - bles and groans with a

bump, bump, bump, The wheels turn - ing ov - er go thump, thump, thump.

Accompany the song by rhythm sticks and wood blocks.

(29)

Playing Train

Ruth Wilson Kelsey

Grace V. Wilson

Come play train, come play train, Cars all in a row; Come play train,

come play train, Hear our whis-tle blow. Ding ding! toot toot toot!

whistle

We go puff-ing by, Ding ding! toot toot toot! Down the track we fly.

whistle

Formation: the children form in lines to represent trains. To accompany the song, the teacher selects instruments which best illustrate train sounds.

The Auto

Mayme Christenson   J. Wolverton

Honk! Honk! Honk! Let's hop in the car for a ride,—With Dad-dy and Moth-er

And Sis-ter and Broth-er And pup-py and kit-ten in-side.—

Honk! Honk! Honk! We're off in the car for a ride!—

NATURE

Autumn

Florence Broad   Florence Broad

1. Gen - tly the trees are sway - ing,
2. Squir - rels are build - ing warm nests,

Soft - ly the leaves flut - ter down,——
Birds of the sum - mer are gone,——

Cov - 'ring the ground with a car - pet,
Flow - ers are sleep - ing in gar - dens,

Red, yel - low, or - ange, and brown.___
Winds sing their soft lull - a - bies.___

The Empty Nest

J. Wolverton
Slowly

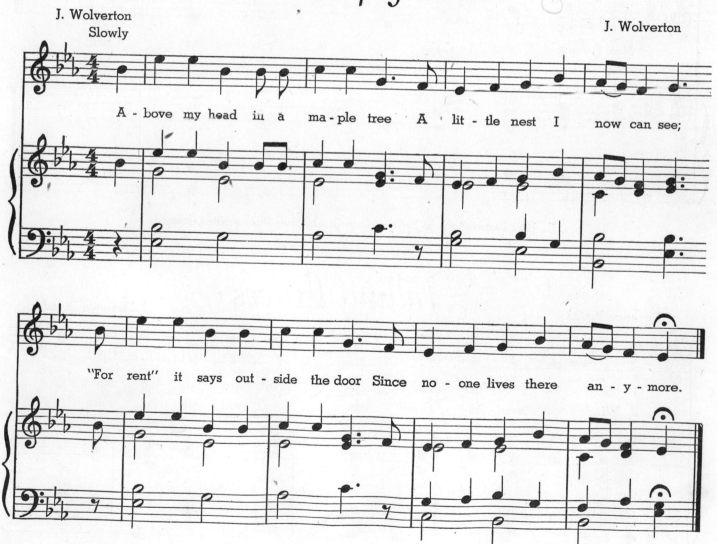

J. Wolverton

A - bove my head in a ma - ple tree A lit - tle nest I now can see;

"For rent" it says out - side the door Since no - one lives there an - y - more.

Leaves

B. Peters

B. Peters

1. New leaves come in spring,
2. Green leaves turn to red,

Mak - ing a shel - ter where rob - ins sing.
Tint - ing the au - tumn trees o - ver - head.

3. Red leaves turn to brown, Late in October they scatter down.

Falling Leaves

Florence Broad

Florence Broad

1. Soft - ly from the tree - tops leaves are fall - ing down,
2. Winds will soon be blow - ing, trees will all be bare,

(34)

They make a love-ly car - pet red and green and brown.
And soon it will be snow - ing, snow-ing ev - 'ry - where.

The Golden Leaves

Mayme Christenson
Smoothly

J. W. Beattie

A gold-en leaf came drift-ing down, And qui-et-ly came whirl-ing,—

Then all at once a hun-dred leaves Came drift-ing down and twirl-ing.——

November Winds

J. W. Beattie

J. W. Beattie

Oo — — — — Hear the No-vem-ber winds blow!—

Oo — — — — Bring-ing us win-ter and snow.—

Wind sounds can be made by dragging the fingernails flat around a drum head.

Coasting

Rose Chadwick

William Dennis

Down the hill we're slid - ing, slid - ing, slid - ing;

See our clip - per glid - ing, A - long the track we go.

Winter

Russel Godfrey

Russel Godfrey

Get your cap, get your coat, Wear your warm - est clothes,

Pull your sled straight a - head Through the win - ter snows.

The North Wind

J. Wolverton

J. Wolverton

Slowly

North wind is blow - ing, Oo —— Hur - ries me on to school, —

Freez - es my fin - gers and nips my toes, Makes me shiv - er and

bites my nose, North wind is blow - ing. Oo —— Oo — Oo —

A Rainy Day

As an accompaniment use rhythm sticks or fingertips on drums.

March

Ruth Wilson Kelsey

Grace V. Wilson

It's March and we hear the wind blow - ing,

Some - times it whis - tles a tune,———

It tells us cold weath - er is go - ing,

That spring will be here ver - y soon.———

Spring Is Here

Mayme Christenson
Moderately fast

German Folk Song

Sun - shine bright, rain - drops light, Make the spring - time flow - ers grow;

Rob - ins sing, voic - es ring: "Hap - py spring is here, we know."

April

Jeannette Gordon

Grace V. Wilson

A - pril, dear A - pril, your blos - soms are sweet; We love your warm sun and soft breeze, We look for the flow - ers that grow at our feet, And hear the birds sing in the trees.

Pussy Willow

Mina Dawson

Mina Dawson

When the first warm breez - es blow Comes a lit - tle friend we know:

Puss - y wil - low, Puss - y wil - low! Then we know that spring is here,

When the fur - ry coats ap - pear, Puss - y wil - low in the spring!

It's Raining

Lorna Hazen

Grace V. Wilson

It's rain - ing, it's rain - ing, It pours from the

sky;—— We're glad that it's rain - ing And we will tell you why:——

The rain helps the gar - dens grow fast - er, you see,——

It's rain - ing, it's rain - ing On ev - 'ry flow'r and tree.——

Raindrop sounds can be made by tapping the fingernails on a drum head.

Working

H. Hinga

French Folk Song

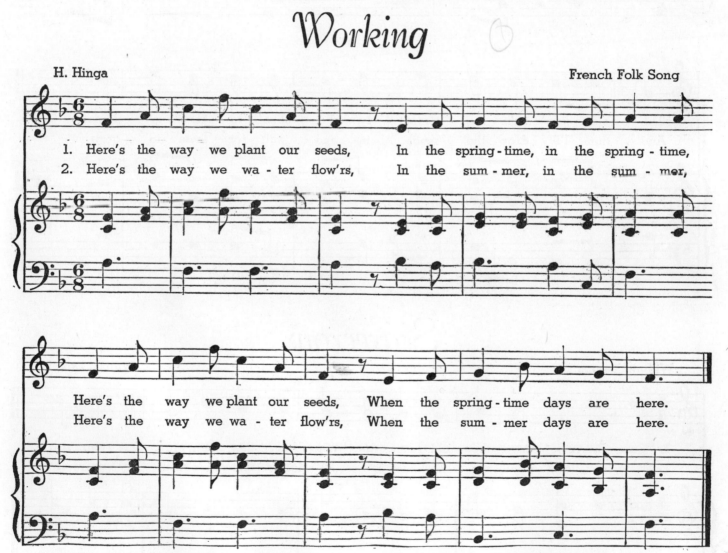

1. Here's the way we plant our seeds, In the spring-time, in the spring-time,
2. Here's the way we wa - ter flow'rs, In the sum - mer, in the sum - mer,

Here's the way we plant our seeds, When the spring-time days are here.
Here's the way we wa - ter flow'rs, When the sum - mer days are here.

3. Here's the way we rake the leaves,
   In the autumn, in the autumn,
   Here's the way we rake the leaves,
   When the autumn days are here.

4. Here's the way we shovel snow,
   In the winter, in the winter,
   Here's the way we shovel snow,
   When the winter days are here.

Planting My Garden

H. Hinga

French Folk Tune

1. I think I'll ask my moth-er if I may spade my gar-den,
2. At first I'll spade the brown earth and rake it ver-y gen-tly,

The sun is shin-ing warm-ly, I'd like to plant my seeds.
And then I'll drop the seeds in and wait for them to grow.

Scarecrow

William Dennis

William Dennis

1. "Caw, caw, caw," cried the old black crow, "Who is that man in my corn row?"
2. "Haw, haw, haw," cried the far-mer low. "I fooled that bird with my scare-crow."

The Robins' Call

Florence Broad

Florence Broad

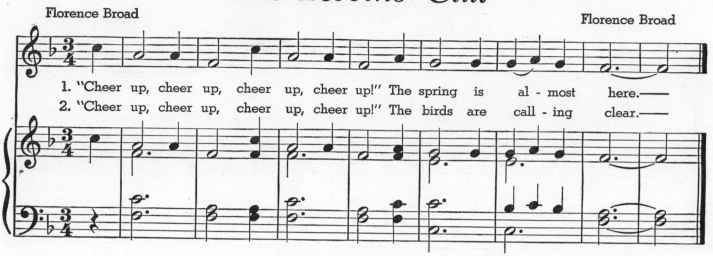

1. "Cheer up, cheer up, cheer up, cheer up!" The spring is al - most here.——
2. "Cheer up, cheer up, cheer up, cheer up!" The birds are call - ing clear.——

Our Garden

Rose Chadwick

William Dennis

1. Man - y kinds of flow - ers grow Bright - ly in our gar - den,
2. Dai - sies, tu - lips, hol - ly - hocks Blos - som in our gar - den,

Dain - ti - ly their fac - es show Nod - ding there at me.
Pan - sies, lil - ies, crim - son phlox Nod and smile at me.

Blackbirds

Russel Godfrey

Russel Godfrey

1. One, two, three, Black-birds three Fly to the limb of a ma-ple tree;
2. Six, seven, eight, Black-birds eight Break off the limb with their heav-y weight;

Four, five, six, What a fix! Not strong e-nough for black-bird tricks.
Eight, nine, ten, Black-birds ten Fly to the ma-ple tree a-gain.

The Bluebird

Cora Nicodemus

Grace V. Wilson

Pret-ty lit-tle blue-bird, Sing a song to me;

While you build your home there In the hol-low tree.

The Seasons

Florence Broad   Florence Broad

1. Things are slow-ly grow - ing, grow - ing, grow - ing,
2. Birds are sweet-ly call - ing, call - ing, call - ing,

Things are slow-ly grow - ing bright in spring.
Birds are sweet-ly call - ing all day long.

3. Leaves are softly falling, falling, falling,
   Leaves are softly falling, red and green.

4. Snow is gently drifting, drifting, drifting,
   Snow is gently drifting, drifting down.

The Little Bird

"Peep!" said the lit-tle bird, "Peep, peep, peep!" said he.

Wading

H. Hinga   H. Hinga

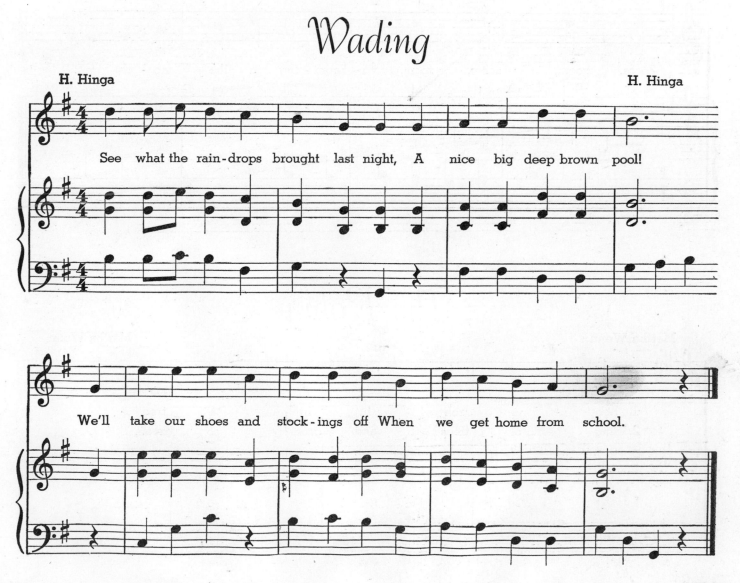

See what the rain-drops brought last night, A nice big deep brown pool!

We'll take our shoes and stock-ings off When we get home from school.

Honeybee

B. Peters

B. Peters

Zoom, zoom, zoom, zoom, Sounds the bus-y hon-ey-bee,

Zoom, zoom, zoom, zoom, Zoom-ing in the ap-ple tree.

The Robin

Martha Wonn

Martha Wonn

1. Rob - in, rob - in in a tree,
2. Sing of trees and grass so green,

Sing a lit - tle song to me, Sing of rain and sun - shine
Sing of clouds that may be seen, Sing of night and sing of

Ending of first stanza   Ending of second stanza

bright, Sing of flow'rs in gold - en light.   Rob - in, rob - in
day, Sing of boys and girls at play.

in a tree, Sing a lit tle song to me.

The Oriole

Martha Wonn

Martha Wonn

An o - ri - ole sits in the old elm tree and

sings and sings and sings, He sits on the edge of his

cra - dle nest and swings and swings and swings.——

SPECIAL DAYS

Funny Witches

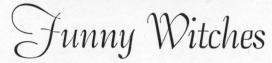

Cora Nicodemus

Grace V. Wilson

Fun - ny witch - es, Tall black hats, Broom - stick hors - es, Big black cats!

Brownies and Witches

Mayme Christenson

J. Wolverton

Mysteriously

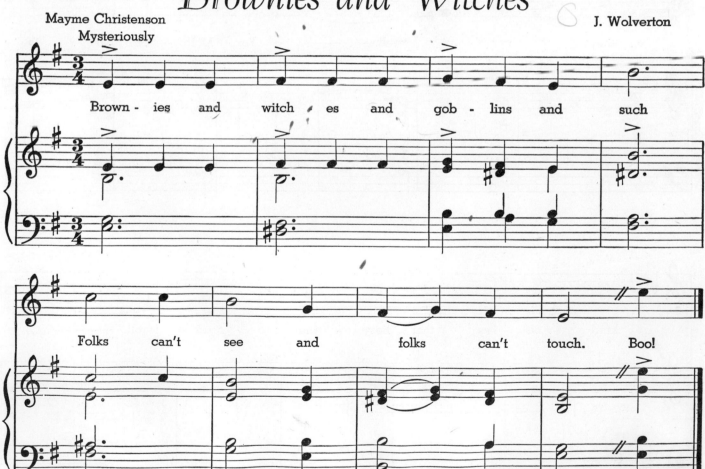

Brown - ies and witch - es and gob - lins and such

Folks can't see and folks can't touch. Boo!

cymbals, gong

Thanksgiving Day

Ruth Wilson Kelsey

Grace V. Wilson

Thanks - giv - ing Day is com - ing soon, I know it ver - y well:——— For Moth - er bakes the kind of pies that have the nic - est smell.———

Pumpkins

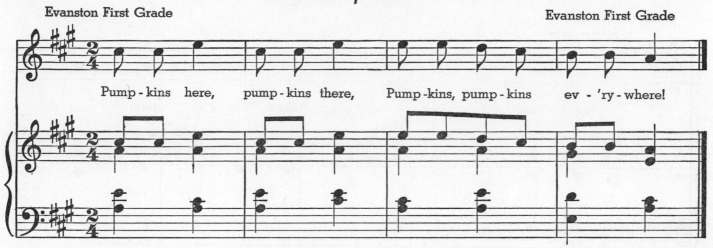

Evanston First Grade

Pump-kins here, pump-kins there, Pump-kins, pump-kins ev-'ry-where!

Gobble!

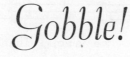

J. Wolverton

Gob-ble! Gob-ble! Who is that? Tur-key gob-bler big and fat.

Gob-ble! Gob-ble! What does he say? Meet me on Thanks-giv-ing Day.

Thanking God

Martha Wonn
Martha Wonn

Thank Him for work and play, Thank Him for night and day,

Thank Him for songs we sing, Thank Him for ev - 'ry - thing.

Christmas Bells

H. Hinga
Old English Tune

The bells in the stee - ple are ring - ing to - day;

I lis - ten and won - der, oh, what do they say?

Come, Moth - er, come, Fath - er, how sweet - ly they chime,

They tell all the peo - ple it's glad Christ - mas time.

The Christmas Tree

Paul P. Foster
Moderately

Wm. Luton Wood

1. What tree is there so fair to see, So love-ly as the Christ-mas tree?
2. And though it blooms but once a year, And ver-y soon must dis-ap-pear,

Left hand

What oth-er hides so man-y joys, On Christmas Eve, for girls and boys?
Of all the trees that you will see, The fin-est is the Christ-mas Tree.

Accompany the song by chimes.

Jingle, Jingle

Mayme Christenson
Lively

Opal Dillon

I hear the bells of San-ta's sleigh: A - jin - gle, jin - gle, jin - gle,

I know that he will come my way, A - jin - gle, jin - gle, jin - gle.

Accompany the song by bells.

Christmas Holidays

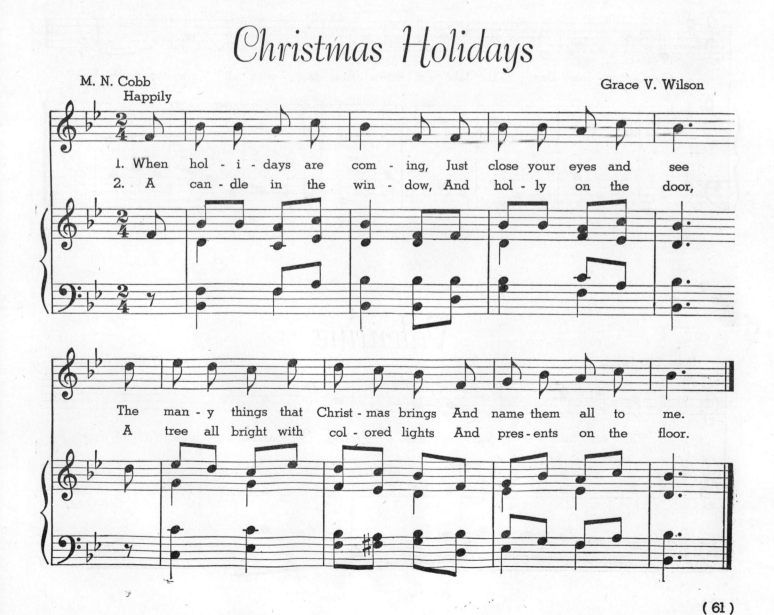

M. N. Cobb

Happily

Grace V. Wilson

1. When hol - i - days are com - ing, Just close your eyes and see
2. A can - dle in the win - dow, And hol - ly on the door,

The man - y things that Christ - mas brings And name them all to me.
A tree all bright with col - ored lights And pres - ents on the floor.

I'll Hang My Stocking

Mayme Christenson

Opal Dillon

Smoothly

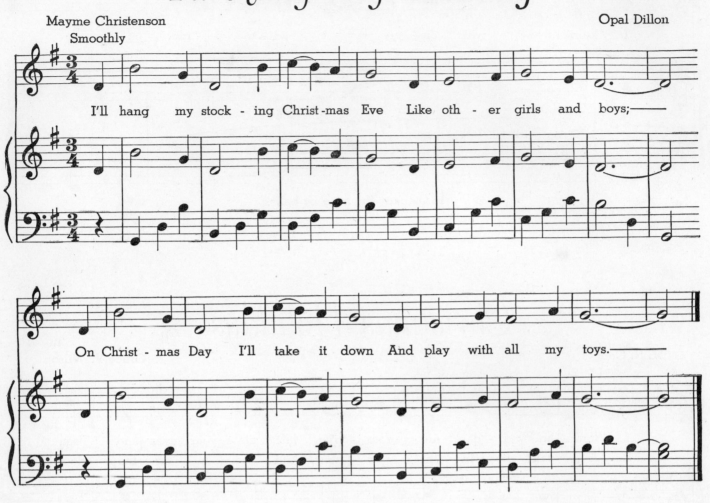

I'll hang my stock-ing Christ-mas Eve Like oth-er girls and boys;——

On Christ-mas Day I'll take it down And play with all my toys.——

Valentine

Rose Chadwick

William Dennis

Val - en - tine, Val - en - tine, Red and blue;

Val - en - tine, Val - en - tine, I love you.

Making Valentines

J. Wolverton

J. Wolverton

One red val - en - tine, Two red val - en - tines, Three red val - en - tines, four;

I'll cut and cut and paste and paste, And then make twen - ty more.

Choruses from Patriotic Songs

1. Battle Hymn of the Republic

Julia Ward Howe

William Steffe

Glo - ry, glo - ry, hal - le - lu - jah! Glo - ry, glo - ry, hal - le - lu - jah!

Glo - ry, glo - ry, hal - le - lu - jah! His truth goes march-ing on.

2. Columbia, the Gem of the Ocean

Timothy Dwight

David T. Shaw

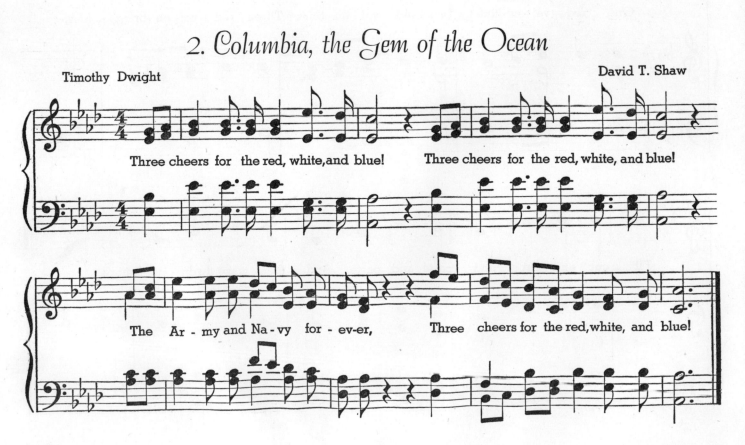

Three cheers for the red, white, and blue! Three cheers for the red, white, and blue!

The Ar - my and Na - vy for - ev-er, Three cheers for the red, white, and blue!

3. The Star-Spangled Banner

Francis Scott Key

John Stafford Smith

Oh, say, does that Star-Span-gled Ban - ner still wave.—

O'er the land of the free and the home of the brave?

Washington and Lincoln

Mina Dawson

Mina Dawson

Smoothly

Wash - ing - ton and Lin - coln, You were both kind and true;

To - day we sing your prais - es And we hon - or you.

Our Flag

Evanston First Grade

Evanston First Grade

We love our flag, our beau-ti-ful flag, The red and white and blue;

We love our flag, our beau-ti-ful flag, The red and white and blue.

My May Basket

Helen Woolfolk

Grace V. Wilson

I'll hang my bas-ket on your door up-on the first of May,

I'll give the bell one ti - ny ring and quick - ly run a - way.

It's Easter Today

Melissa Murphy

German Folk Song

Hap - py chil - dren, lift your voic - es, Join the cho - rus ris - ing

gay; Win - ter's o - ver, Spring has found us And it's East - er to - day!

THE FARM
Ducks

Adapted
Brightly

German Folk Song

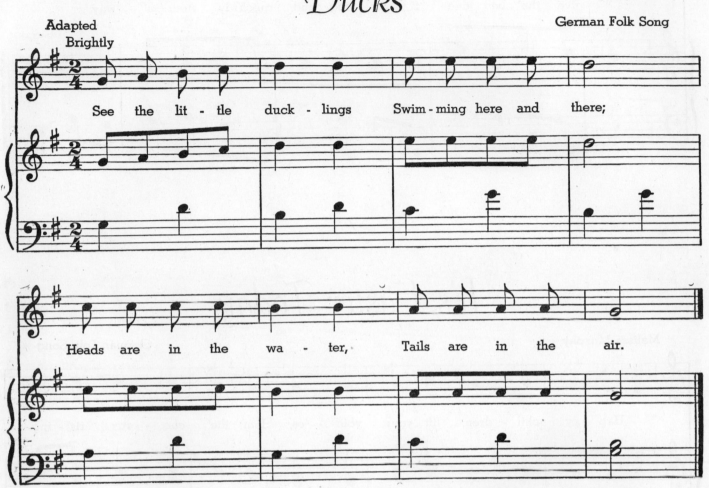

See the lit-tle duck-lings Swim-ming here and there;

Heads are in the wa-ter, Tails are in the air.

Use wood blocks and rhythm sticks as an accompaniment.

Little Sheep

Translated

French Folk Song

What a pret-ty sheep have I, She's the nic-est one of all,

Through the gate I now must send her, For I can no long-er tend her,

Let your sheep no long-er roam, Call them in and take them home.

Chickens and Ducks

Alma Spear

Alma Spear

Lit - tle chick - ens say, "Peep-peep." Un - der Moth - er's wings they creep.
Lit - tle duck - lings say, "Quack-quack," Climb - ing on their Moth - er's back.

At Market

Translated
Gaily

Provençal Singing Game

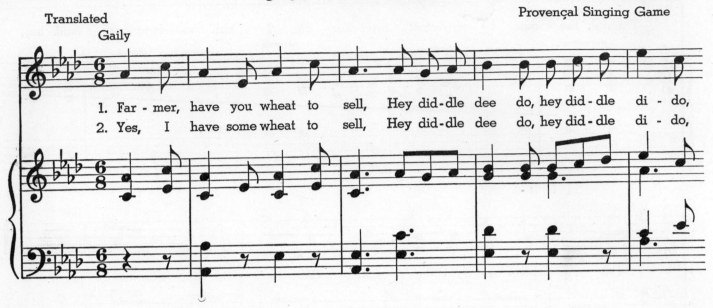

1. Far - mer, have you wheat to sell, Hey did-dle dee do, hey did - dle di - do,
2. Yes, I have some wheat to sell, Hey did-dle dee do, hey did - dle di - do,

Far - mer, have you wheat to sell? O - pen your sack and we'll pay you well.
Yes, I have some wheat to sell, Here is my sack, you have paid me well.

3. Farmer, have you oats to sell, etc.
4. Yes, I have some oats to sell, etc.
5. Farmer, have you corn to sell, etc.
6. Yes, I have some corn to sell, etc.

Divide the class into a line of farmers and a line of buyers. The two lines sit on the floor, each buyer opposite a farmer. The buyers sing the first stanza. At "Open your sack" the farmers go through the motions of opening a bag. They then sing the second stanza. At "Here is my sack" the buyers pretend to pay them. The game continues in this fashion, buyers and farmers singing alternate lines. The children will think of various other products, such as eggs, milk, apples, and the like.

The Farmer

1. Shall I show you how the farm - er, Shall I show you how the farm - er,
2. Oh, it's this way that the farm - er, Oh, it's this way that the farm - er,
3. Shall I show you how the farm - er, Shall I show you how the farm - er,
4. Oh, it's this way that the farm - er, Oh, it's this way that the farm - er,
5. Shall I show you how the farm - er, Shall I show you how the farm - er,
6. Oh, it's this way that the farm - er, Oh, it's this way that the farm - er,

Shall I show you how the farm - er Sows his bar - ley and wheat?
Oh, it's this way that the farm - er Sows his bar - ley and wheat!
Shall I show you how the farm - er Mows his bar - ley and wheat?
Oh, it's this way that the farm - er Mows his bar - ley and wheat!
Shall I show you how the farm - er Thresh - es bar - ley and wheat?
Oh, it's this way that the farm - er Thresh - es bar - ley and wheat!

The children form three groups—A, B, and C. All sing the first stanza. Groups A and B sing the second stanza while Group C performs the action suggested by the words; i.e., the children fold their left arms across their breasts to represent sacks of grain and with their right hands take grain out of the sacks and scatter it. All the children sing the third stanza. Groups B and C sing the fourth stanza while Group A goes through the motions of reaping; i.e., the children hold imaginary plants with their left hands, cutting them with make-believe scythes held in their right hands. All sing the fifth stanza. Groups C and A sing the sixth stanza while Group B performs the action of threshing with a flail, stamping at the same time.

Higgeldy Piggeldy

Nursery Rhyme
Lively

J. Wolverton

Hig-gel-dy pig-gel-dy, my black hen, She lays eggs for gen-tle-men:

Some-times nine, and some-times ten, Hig-gel-dy pig-gel-dy, my black hen.

Rooster's Call

B. Peters
Gaily

B. Peters

"Cock - a - doo - dle - doo!" Hear the roost - er call to you,——

Get up, he is giv - ing a warn - ing;—

"Cock - a - doo - dle - doo!" Hear the roost - er call to you,—

Get up, it's a fine sun - ny morn - ing.—

Feeding the Animals

Mayme Christenson

J. Wolverton

Moderately

1. I can - not feed the an - i - mals When I go to the zoo,
2. I like to feed the ba - by chicks That I buy at the store,

But if I were a farm - er boy, I know what I would do:
But if I were a farm - er girl I could have man - y more:

"Come pig, come pig, come pig, come pig, Come pig, pig, pig," I'd call;
"Come chick, etc.

And when the pigs come run-ning here, I'd give some food to all.
chicks

Cows and Sheep

Mina Dawson

Mina Dawson

Smoothly

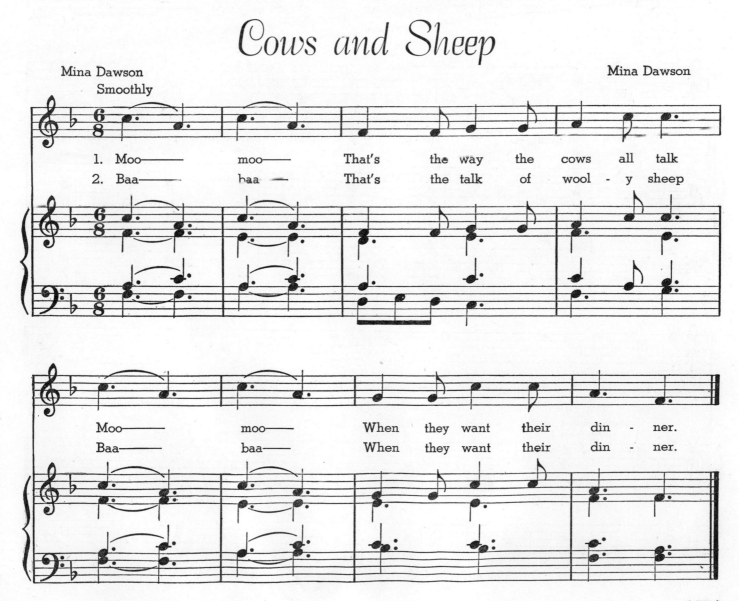

1. Moo——— moo——— That's the way the cows all talk
2. Baa——— baa——— That's the talk of wool-y sheep

Moo——— moo——— When they want their din-ner.
Baa——— baa——— When they want their din-ner.

A Farmer Went Riding

Folk Rhyme

Well accented

Old Tune

1. A far - mer went rid - ing up - on his gray mare,
2. A ra - ven cried, "Croak" and they all tum - bled down,

Bump - e - ty, bump - e - ty bump!——— With his daugh - ter be - side him so
Bump - e - ty, bump - e - ty bump!——— The mare broke her knees and the

ros - y and fair, Lump - e - ty, lump - e - ty lump!———
far - mer his crown, Lump - e - ty, lump - e - ty lump!———

Use a wood-block accompaniment to the song.

ANIMALS

Fluffy

Waco children

Waco children

Fluf - fy is a lit - tle squirrel, He lives in a tree;

I like Fluf - fy, And Fluf - fy likes me.

Skipper

J. W. Beattie

Lively

J. W. Beattie

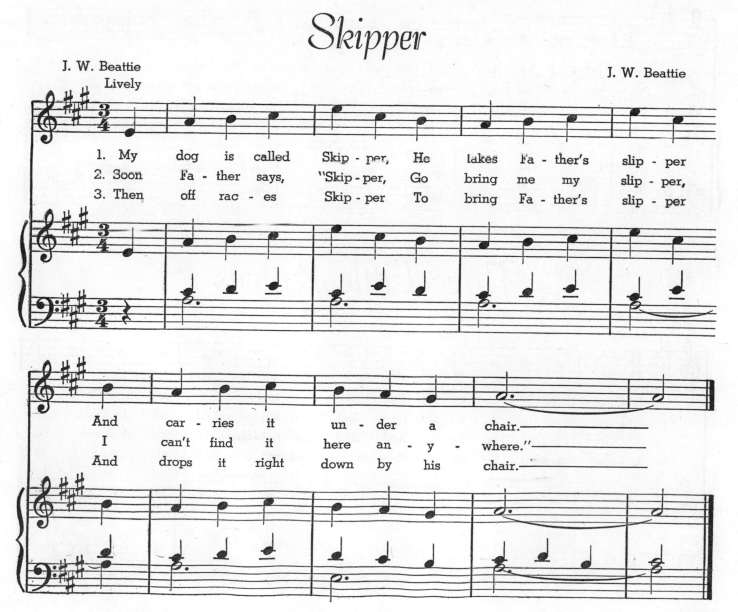

1. My dog is called Skip - per, He takes Fa - ther's slip - per
2. Soon Fa - ther says, "Skip - per, Go bring me my slip - per,
3. Then off rac - es Skip - per To bring Fa - ther's slip - per

And car - ries it un - der a chair.
I can't find it here an - y - where."
And drops it right down by his chair.

(77)

Squirrel Has a Bushy Tail

American Folk Song

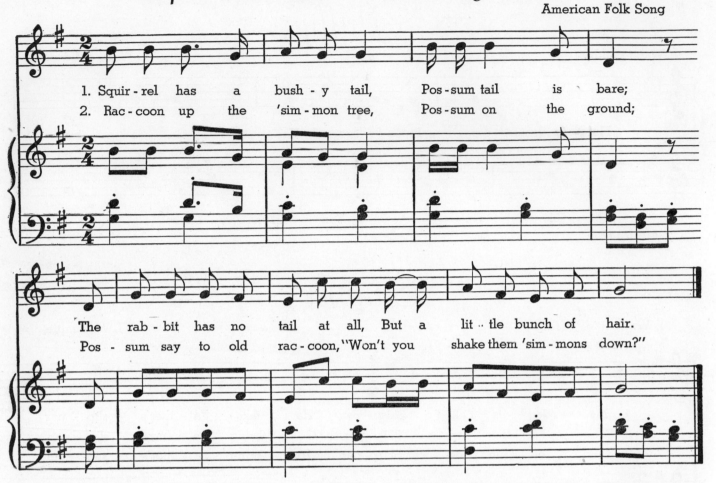

1. Squir-rel has a bush-y tail, Pos-sum tail is bare;
2. Rac-coon up the 'sim-mon tree, Pos-sum on the ground;

The rab-bit has no tail at all, But a lit-tle bunch of hair.
Pos-sum say to old rac-coon, "Won't you shake them 'sim-mons down?"

Three Little Kittens

Nursery Rime
Lively

Old English Tune

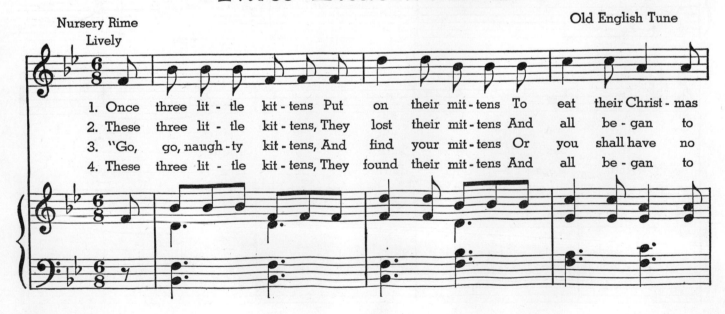

1. Once three lit-tle kit-tens Put on their mit-tens To eat their Christ-mas
2. These three lit-tle kit-tens, They lost their mit-tens And all be-gan to
3. "Go, go, naugh-ty kit-tens, And find your mit-tens Or you shall have no
4. These three lit-tle kit-tens, They found their mit-tens And all be-gan to

pie,— Meow, meow, meow, meow, To eat their Christ - mas pie.
cry,— Meow, meow, meow, meow, They all be - gan to cry.
pie,— Meow, meow, meow, meow, Or you shall have no pie."
cry,— "Meow, meow, meow, meow, Now we can have some pie!"

My Wish

H. Hinga   French Folk Tune

I wish I had a po - ny with coal of shin - y black,

I'd hur - ry home from school and ride up - on his back.

Old Mister Elephant

J. Wolverton

J. Wolverton

Old Mis-ter El-e-phant, wrin-kled and gray, Old Mis-ter El-e-phant walks this way: Swing-ing his trunk and swing-ing his tail, Swing-ing a-long on the jun-gle trail. Old Mis-ter El-e-phant,

wrin-kled and gray, Old Mis - ter El - e - phant walks this way.

As an accompaniment, beat the drum head with the whole hand.

Cat and Bird

B. Peters   B. Peters

A cat shouldwear a lit-tle bell That tin-kles ver-y, ver-y clear,

So all the birds can sure-ly tell When an-y hun-gry cat is near.

The Toad

William Dennis

William Dennis

The old brown toad is a fun-ny-look-ing thing, With his

stead-y hop-hop-hop; He can-not fly, for he

has no tail or wing But he gets there, flop-flop-flop!

The Boy and the Billy Goats Three

A Folk Story Based upon Folk Music

Once upon a time there was a boy who had three billy goats. Every morning he would take them up the hill to eat grass.

Come with Me, My Billy Goats Three

Brightly

Folk Tune

Come with me, my bil - ly goats three, Up on the hill - side

Where the grass is fresh and green; O come with me up the hill - side.

(Repeat the music for climbing. The knees should be lifted high in climbing.)

One morning he was very tired and sleepy. He sat down under a tree.

I'll Rest and Sleep

Softly, slowly

Folk Tune

I'll rest and sleep be - neath this tree; Go, bil - ly goats, a -

slower

way from me. Ho hum, Ho hum, Ho hum. (yawns)

And soon he was fast asleep. But the billy goats three were not tired and sleepy. They were very hungry.

They Ran All About

Lively

Folk Tune

They ran and they ran and they ran all a - bout,

Ran all a-bout, ran all a-bout; They came to a field where the

corn was tall, They jumped, jumped o-ver the wall.

(The movement is in galloping rhythm.)

After a while the boy woke up and rubbed his eyes.
"Where am I? And where are my billy goats three?"

Yoo Hoo!

Boy: Yoo hoo! Yoo hoo! Yoo hoo!— Goats: Baa baa! Baa baa! Baa baa!—

Boy: Come here, come here, billy goats three!
Goats: Baa baa! We like this corn to eat.
　　　We're going to stay here all day and eat and eat.
Boy: Then I will drive you out!

They Ran All About

Folk Tune

Lively

They ran and they ran and they ran all a-bout, Ran all a-bout, ran all a-bout.

Boy:

"I can't drive them out, oh, what shall I do? Boo hoo! What shall I do?"

The boy sat down under the tree and cried and cried.

Rabbit Came a-Hopping

Folk Tune

Brightly, well accented

Rab - bit came a - hop - ping, a - hop - ping, a - hop - ping;

Rab - bit came a - hop - ping And stopped be - neath the tree.

Rabbit: Boy (mournfully):

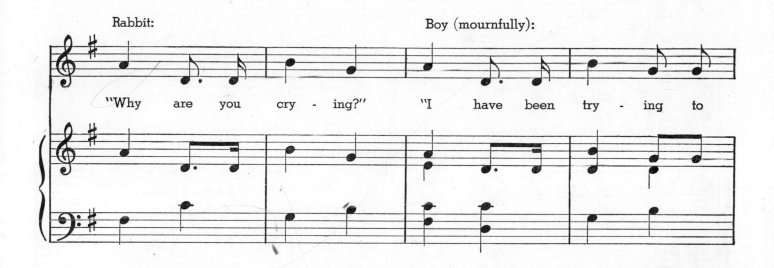

"Why are you cry - ing?" "I have been try - ing to

Rabbit (boastfully):

drive my goats a - way from there." "Then leave the job to me!"

Rabbit: Come here, come here, billy goats three!

Goats: Baa! We like this corn to eat. We're going to stay here all day and eat and eat.

Rabbit: Then I will drive you out!

They Ran All About

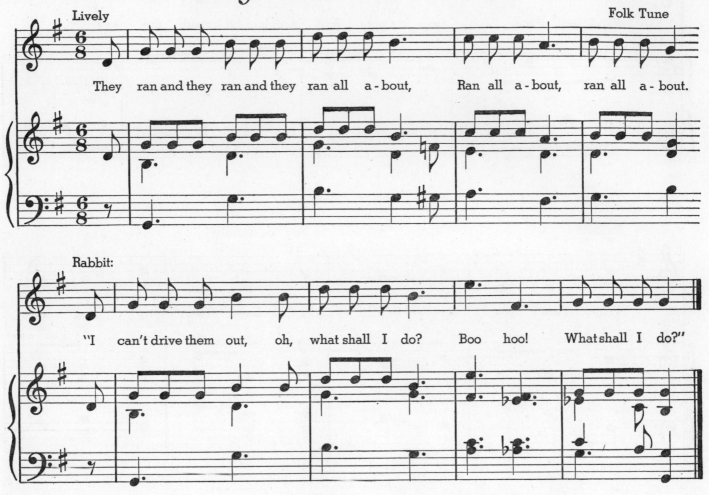

So Mister Rabbit sat down under the tree beside the boy and cried and cried.

Fox Came a-Loping

Mis - ter Fox came lop - ing and stopped be-neath the tree.

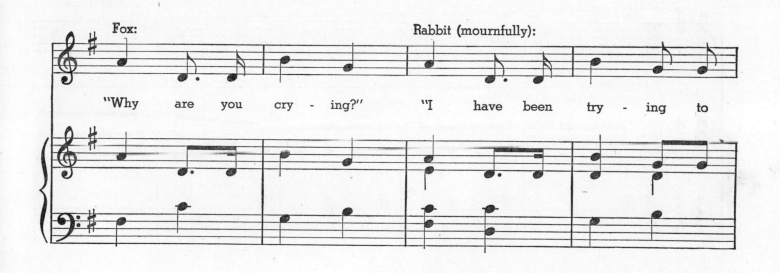

Fox: "Why are you cry - ing?" Rabbit (mournfully): "I have been try - ing to

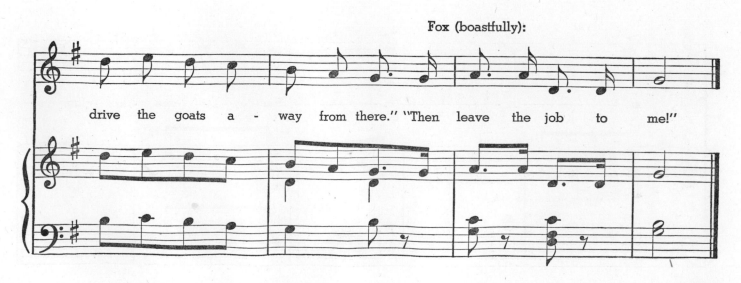

drive the goats a - way from there." Fox (boastfully): "Then leave the job to me!"

Fox: Come here, come here, billy goats three!

Goats: Baa baa! We like this corn to eat. We're going to stay here all day and eat and eat.

Fox: Then I will drive you out!

Song: They ran and they ran and they ran all about,

    Ran all about, ran all about.

      (Fox) "I can't drive them out, oh, what shall I do?

      Boo hoo! What shall I do?"

So Mister Fox sat down under the tree beside the boy and Mister Rabbit and cried and cried.

Honeybee Came Buzzing

buzz - ing, a - buzz - ing, Hon - ey - bee came buzz - ing And

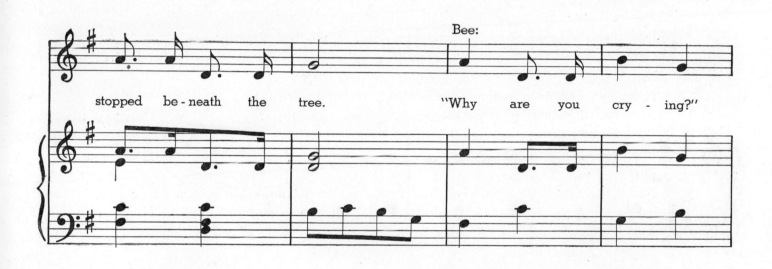

stopped be - neath the tree. Bee: "Why are you cry - ing?"

Fox: "I have been try - ing to drive the goats a - way from there."

Bee:

"Then leave this job to me!" Zz —— Zz —— Zz —— Zz ——

hold pedal down

(A buzzing chorus of voices throughout)

Boy
Rabbit }: You are too small. You cannot drive the goats out of the field of corn.
Fox

Bee: Then I will show you how! Come here, come here, billy goats three!

Goats: Baa baa! We like this corn to eat. We're going to stay here all day and eat and eat.

Bee: Then I will drive you out!

Song: The bee flew in and they ran all about,

    Ran all about, ran all about.

    He flew in their hair and stung them all,

    They jumped back over the wall.

Boy
Fox }: Oh, thank you, honeybee, for driving the goats out of the field of corn.
Rabbit

Song: Come with me, my billy goats three,

    Up on the hillside,

    Where the grass is fresh and green,

    Oh, come with me up the hillside.

THE END

GAMES
Round the Village

English Game Song

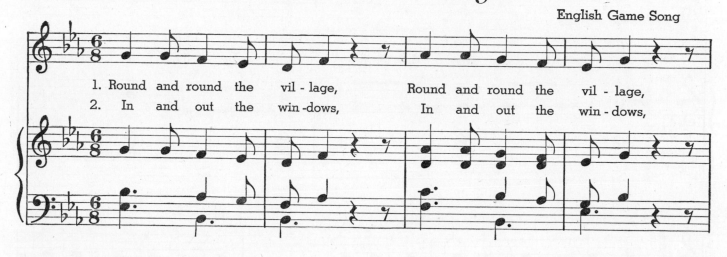

1. Round and round the vil - lage, Round and round the vil - lage,
2. In and out the win -dows, In and out the win - dows,

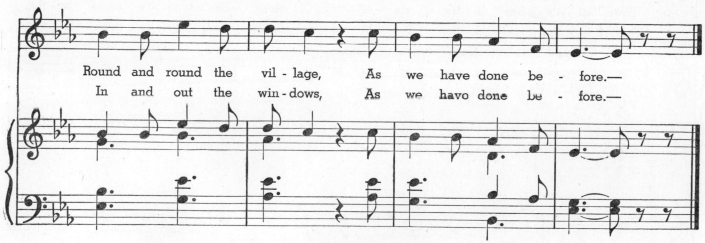

Round and round the vil - lage, As we have done be - fore.—
In and out the win -dows, As we havo done be - fore.—

3. Stand and face your partner, etc.
4. Follow him (her) to London, etc.
5. Shake your hand and leave him (her), etc.

The children form two circles, one inside the other. (1) The inner circle stands still and sings the first stanza while the outer circle marches around it. (2) The outer circle stands still and sings the second stanza while the children in the inner circle weave "in and out the windows," which are formed by the players in the outer circle, standing well apart. (3) Both circles stand still and face each other, all players singing and making a low bow on the words "As we have done before." (4) The outer circle, standing still, sings the fourth stanza while the inner circle marches around. (5) During the fifth stanza the inner circle stands still and sings. The children in the outer circle, marching around it, wave their hands in farewell.

Ten Little Indians

Old Song

1. One lit-tle, two lit-tle, three lit-tle In-dians,
2. Ten lit-tle, nine lit-tle, eight lit-tle In-dians,

Four lit-tle, five lit-tle, six lit-tle In-dians, Sev'n lit-tle, eight lit-tle,
Sev'n lit-tle, six lit-tle, five lit-tle In-dians, Four lit-tle, three lit-tle,

nine lit-tle In-dians, Ten lit-tle In-dian boys.
two lit-tle In-dians, One lit-tle In-dian boy.

Ten boys stand in a row, facing the class. They "number off" from 1 to 10, until each is sure of his own number identity. The rest of the class sing the song. As each number is sung, the boy to whom the number belongs takes one long step forward, forming a new line which is completed when the first verse has been sung. As the class sings the second verse, reverse the process by having each boy step back one step, thus forming the original line. The class repeats the song as the ten boys turn and march around the room. Vary the game by having "Indian girls" form the line.

Bounce Around

American Folk Song

2. Close up the schoolroom to-day, etc.,
   Long summer day.

3. Open the schoolroom to-day, etc.,
   Long summer day.

Directions: Circle Game

The players join hands and form a circle.

While singing the refrain, they dance around as fast as they can.

While singing stanza 1, they walk demurely.

The refrain is sung again, and they fly around as before.

Singing stanza 2, they all walk toward the center, forming as compact a group as possible, with hands held high and close.

Singing stanza 3, they widen the ring out again to its original size.

The game ends with a repetition of the refrain, the children flying around as at the beginning.

The Mulberry Bush

Moderately

Traditional Game Song

1. Here we go round the mul-ber-ry bush, the mul-ber-ry bush,
2. This is the way we wash our clothes, we wash our clothes,
3. This is the way we i-ron our clothes, we i-ron our clothes,
4. This is the way we scrub the floor, we scrub the floor,
5. This is the way we mend our clothes, we mend our clothes,
6. This is the way we sweep the house, we sweep the house,
7. Thus do we play when work is done, when work is done,

the mul-ber-ry bush, Here we go round the mul-ber-ry bush,
we wash our clothes, This is the way we wash our clothes,
we i-ron our clothes, This is the way we i-ron our clothes,
we scrub the floor, This is the way we scrub the floor,
we mend our clothes, This is the way we mend our clothes,
we sweep the house, This is the way we sweep the house,
when work is done, Thus do we play when work is done,

So ear-ly in the morn-ing.
So ear-ly Mon-day morn-ing.
So ear-ly Tues-day morn-ing.
So ear-ly Wednes-day morn-ing.
So ear-ly Thurs-day morn-ing.
So ear-ly Fri-day morn-ing.
So ear-ly Sat-ur-day morn-ing.

The players form a circle and join hands. They move to the left as they sing the first stanza. Then they stand still, drop hands, and go through the motions indicated by the lines as they sing stanzas 2–7.

Looby Loo

English Game Song

Refrain:
Here we dance loo - by loo, — Here we dance loo - by light, —

Here we dance loo - by loo, — All on a Sat - ur - day night. —

Stanza:
1. I put my right hand in, — I put my right hand out, —
2. I put my left hand in, — I put my left hand out, —

I give my right hand a shake, shake, shake And turn my - self a - bout. —
I give my left hand a shake, shake, shake And turn my - self a - bout. —

3. I put my right foot in, etc.
4. I put my left foot in, etc.
5. I put my whole self in, etc.

The children form a circle and join hands. During the chorus they move to the left, stopping at "Saturday night." For the five stanzas of the song they suit the action to the word and go through the motions suggested by the text. After each stanza they join hands, repeat the chorus, and move to the left.

The Shoemaker

Traditional Game Song

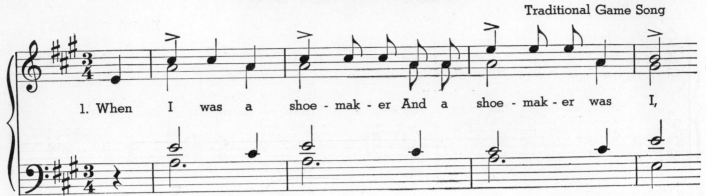

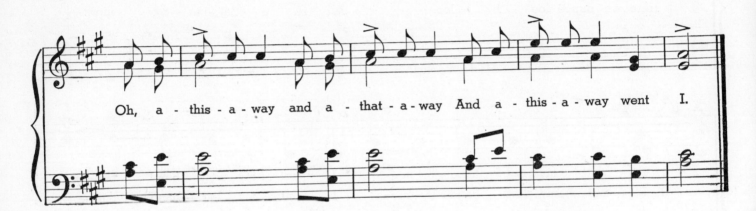

2. When I was a tailor, etc.

3. When I was a farmer, etc.

4. When I was a drummer, etc.

5. When I was a pilot, etc.

This game may be played with the children standing or seated. All the children sing the song. While singing the second line they go through the motions suggested by the words. For instance, for the shoemaker they tap; for the tailor, move their right arms in a sewing motion. Get the children to suggest other occupations.

Dance, Thumbkin, Dance

English Game Song

1. Dance, thumb-kin, dance; Dance, thumb-kin, dance; Thumb-kin can-not dance a-lone, So dance, my mer-ry men, ev-'ry one, And dance, thumb-kin, dance.

Finger Game: (1) thumb; (2) forefinger (foreman), etc.

2. Dance, foreman, dance, etc.

3. Dance, long man, dance, etc.

4. Dance, ring man, dance, etc.

5. Dance, little man, dance, etc.

Seven Steps

(Circle Dance)

Adapted

Austrian Folk Tune

One, two, three, four, five, six, sev'n; One, two, three, four, five, six, sev'n;

Move forward 7 steps and jump.   Move backward 7 steps and jump.

One, two, three, One, two, three; One, two, three, four, five, six, sev'n; five, six, sev'n.

Move to right and jump.   Move to left and jump.   (1) Turn to right and (2) Turn to left and   jump.   jump.

Dancing in a Ring

(Circle Dance)

Adapted

Swedish Folk Tune

Some - one is walk-ing slow-ly a - round the ring, a - round the ring,

Child walks around ring.

Now who will be the part-ner to dance with her and sing?
(him)

Takes partner.

Tra la la la, Tra la la la la, Tra la la la, Tra la la la la,

All skip around in circle formation.

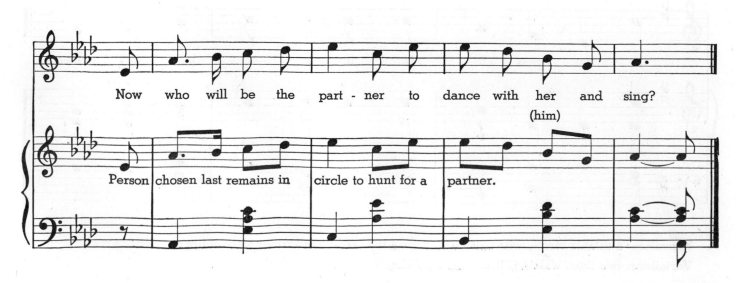

Now who will be the part-ner to dance with her and sing?
(him)

Person chosen last remains in circle to hunt for a partner.

We're Going Home

Adapted

Danish Folk Song

Walking tempo

Now we're go - ing home, Now we're go - ing home. It

is, it is a long way home. Now we're go - ing home, Now we're

go - ing home, It is, it is a long way home.

Formation: a double circle, with one circle inside the other. The circles walk in opposite directions.

Variations: two lines walking, three lines walking.

Song Fragments for Retarded Singers

On page 3, specific aids for retarded singers were presented. Such aids usually suggest matching single tones, employing neutral syllables "too, yoo, boo," etc. As soon as children can form word syllables on successions of tones, teachers should use short phrases containing series. Many songs in this book are especially helpful for this purpose, since they provide teachers with short phrases based upon one-, two-, and three-tone patterns. These phrases may be isolated from the songs and used as tonal exercises for children who cannot yet sing entire melodies.

ONE-TONE PHRASES

Telephone, p. 9, "Ting-a-ling-a-ling"
Scissors Grinders' Bell, 19, "Ring ding ding"
Traffic Man, 19, "Old Pat Moran"
Fire Department, 22, "Cling, cling, cling"
Be Careful, 25, "Stop, look, listen"
Transportation, 27, "Choo-choo" etc.
Scarecrow, 46, "Caw, caw, caw"
Honey Bee, 52, "Zoom, zoom, zoom, zoom"
Rooster's Call, 72, "Cock-a-doodle-doo"
Apples, 171, "Apples, apples in the tree"
Auto Horns, 172, "Honk! Honk! Honk!"

TWO-TONE PHRASES

Calling, p. 6, "Hello, hello, hello!"

Sleepy Time, 7, "Bylo, lullaby"
School Time, 15, "Ding, dong, ding, dong!"
Postman, 23, "Here comes the postman"
Conductor's Call, 26, "All aboard! all aboard!"
Winter, 37, "Get your cap, get your coat"
North Wind, 38, "Oo, oo, oo"
Pumpkins, 57, "Pumpkins here, pumpkins there"
Gobble, 57, "Gobble! Gobble! Who is that?"
Cows and Sheep, 75, "Moo, moo"
Train, 171, "Choo-choo, says the train"
Clock, 172, "Tick, tock, tick, tock"

THREE-TONE PHRASES

Good Morning, p. 18, "Good morning, good morning"
Shopping, 22, "Mister Grocer, tell me please"
Crossing the Street, 25, "Look to the left! Look to the right!"
Spring Is Here, 41, "Sunshine bright, raindrops light"
Robins' Call, 47, "Cheer up, cheer up" etc.
Funny Witches, 66, "Funny witches, tall black hats"
Valentine, 62, "Valentine, valentine"
Chickens and Ducks, 69, "Little chickens say, Peep-peep"
Feeding the Animals, 74, "Come pig, come pig" etc.
Engine, 172, entire song

Rest and Relaxation

The need for periods of relaxation for children in these strenuous times is recognized by every teacher. The only problem is to get the children to relax when the period arrives. Lying in one spot, tense as a coiled spring that is ready to pop up at the signal for release, can hardly be called relaxation. Some standards of measurement of lesser and lesser degrees of tension need to be built up in the understanding of children if we expect their co-operation in so intangible a thing as relaxation.

Visual aids such as a rag doll that "cannot move by itself," a sleepy kitten, or a very co-operative child can demonstrate how a relaxed arm and leg look when lifted and shaken and dropped back to the floor again. When the children try to do this, the teacher may go around and check the degree of relaxation. Later on, children may be chosen to go around and check the other children for relaxation, if they can do it with sufficient calmness. The children can learn to do the checking for relaxation themselves by shaking an arm or leg less and less strenuously until finally it is ready to drop and stay relaxed. If they do this in a fairly uniform way to musical accompaniment, the eventual result should be a relaxed group before the period is over.

Night Time

J. Wolverton

(Sung by teacher)

J. Wolverton

Simply and slowly

Yawning

At night when I'm sleep - y, There's some-thing in - side makes me
yawn and yawn and yawn.—— My jaws start to o - pen my
mouth ver - y wide And I yawn and yawn and yawn.——

The Rag Doll

(Sung by teacher)

J. Wolverton

J. Wolverton

Deliberately

I'm just a rag doll, so limp - e - ty limp, My

bod - y is made with - out bones;——— My head, my neck, my

arms, my feet Are heav - y, as heav - y as stones;——— I'm

just a rag doll, so limp-e-ty limp, So limp-e-ty, limp-e-ty limp.——

Lazy Mary

Nina Dawson

Nina Dawson

Very slowly

La - zy Ma - ry, all tired out, Does-n't care to move a - bout,

Can't get up, can't get down, La - zi - est girl in all the town.

Vary the name, using "Tommy," "Jimmy," etc.

Choral

(Listening)

Schumann

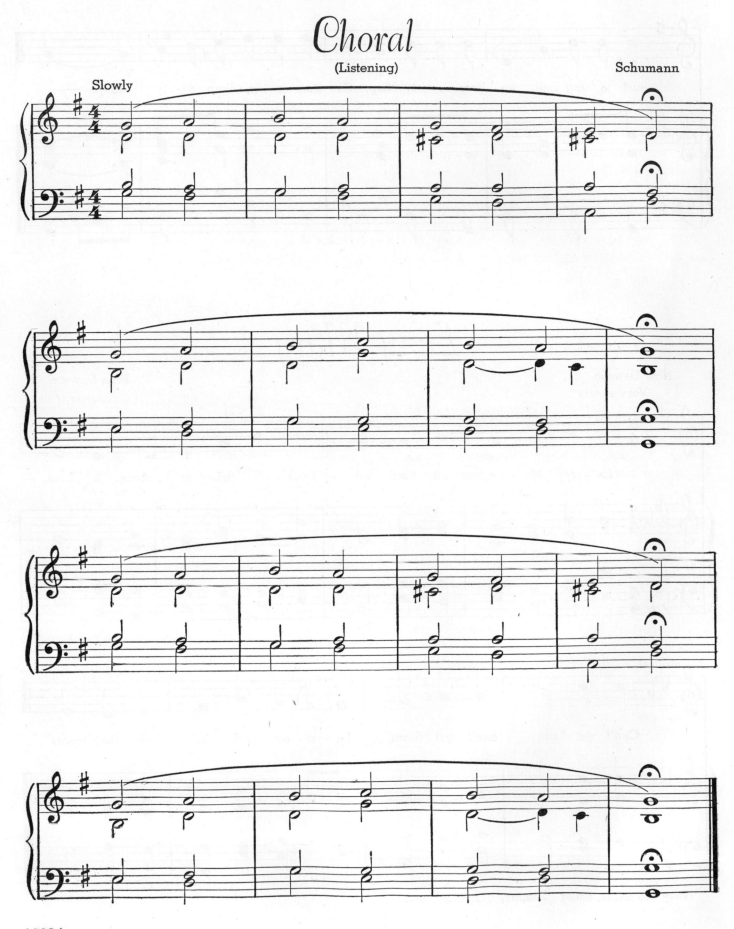

Rhythm

Rhythmic clarity is as important to the beauty of good singing as is tonal clarity. Most music teachers will work to achieve tonal clarity without feeling any need to work to achieve the same kind of rhythmic clarity. Rather than develop the group rhythmically the teacher gives them, or rather tries to give them, the rhythm by rote methods. Real rhythmic awareness can come only from remembering the feeling of rhythmic movement as you have had it yourself. No one can give you that feeling or take it away from you. Without that feeling, analysis of rhythmic form is difficult and stilted; with it, there is ease and naturalness. If the proper job of training in rhythmic fundamentals and note reading is done in the first four grades, the children should be ready for part singing in the upper four grades.

It is the object of this series of books to set up such a progression in rhythmic training. This first book begins by building an awareness of moderate timing and intensity, upon which is based a survey of the possibilities of variation to faster and slower timing and to louder and softer intensities.

Free Rhythmic Movement to Musical Accompaniment

A good "sense of rhythm" is a good awareness of rhythm. Through rhythmic movement in the kindergarten and first grade the child acquires this experience. As we have learned from psychologists, our awareness must be kept alive and growing through the introduction of new factors. Therefore the teacher in accompanying rhythmic movement should not use the same materials repeatedly without change or progressive enrichment. What challenge and growth is there for the child who has to skip to the same music in the same way day after day for a whole semester? A good teacher will not only vary the kind of accompaniment from piano to voice and to percussion but will also see that it is varied rhythmically to suggest variations in the rhythmic movement. For example, tempo can be gradually speeded up almost to a run. All rhythmic movements can be used to develop an awareness of rhythm by such devices as the following:

1. Change of Time Intervals (the speed of the basic beat)
a. From moderate to very fast as direct contrast
b. From moderate to very fast as gradual change
c. From moderate to very slow as direct contrast
d. From moderate to very slow as gradual change
e. From very slow to very fast as direct contrast
f. From very slow to very fast as gradual change
g. From moderate to fast to slow in short sequences

2. Change of Intensity Values (the volume of the sound made)
a. From moderate to very soft as direct contrast
b. From moderate to very soft as gradual change
c. From moderate to very loud as direct contrast
d. From moderate to very loud as gradual change
e. From very soft to very loud as direct contrast
f. From very soft to very loud as gradual change
g. From moderate to soft and loud in short sequences

3. Change of Direction of the Movement in the Room
a. Forward and backward alternately
b. To the right and the left side alternately
c. Circularly in either direction
d. Upward or downward
e. Any combinations of these in varying sequences

4. Change of Grouping (relationship of each child to the space in the room and to the other individuals in it)
a. As individuals scattered around the room in even spacing
b. As individuals massed in one section of the room
c. As individuals in a single or double or loosely formed circle
d. As individuals in a line one in back of the other or side by side
e. As couples; facing, back to back, side to side, or following
f. As threes; in line or circle formation
g. As fours; in any of the above formations

When a child comes to school, he is already fairly expert in many of the commoner rhythmic movements and is ready to learn new things about them. The name of the movement is the first thing that should be learned by attaching it to the movement. Next, some basic ideas of good qualities of execution of the movements should be built up as standards of perfection toward which the child is to aim. These are mentioned in a form simple enough to be used with children in connection with each of the movements.

Often the teacher of small children is handicapped by not having adequate space for movement for the whole group. Lack of space need not become a reason for leaving out all movement. Small groups in succession, or even individuals in succession, could use whatever space there is at the front or back of the room, or up and down the aisles. An ingenious teacher will always find a way to adapt this material to her own situation, so that the children will not miss the opportunity of developing a good sense of rhythm at the time when it is most desirable that they do so.

Spoken Chants for Accompanying Rhythmic Movement

The young child tends to have some vocal accompaniment for everything he does. It is a natural accompaniment which has the same timing and intensity as the movement and is motivated from the same source. Most of this vocalization is at the speaking or chanting level, but it is the raw material out of which song can be made. Teachers tend to suppress this spontaneous creative material as noise rather than to utilize it as a source for original verse and song. Whenever it accompanies rhythmic movement, it will be rhythmic in character. Whether or not it is rhymed in its finished form is of minor importance, so long as it

has a strong rhythmic quality. When a pleasing verse is found and used by the group it will gradually develop a natural inflectional pattern. This pattern of pitch variation can become the basis for an accompanying melody to complete the process of "making up" a song. Any group, if given enough encouragement and opportunity, can make up a little book of songs in this way around the theme of a season, a project, or the hobby of the individual child.

Some samples of the simplest rhythmic chants are given with each of the movements. Many of these have been done by children, as is indicated; some have been done by the teachers of children; and the rest are from the poets who have written for children in the past and the present. They are all cast in the rhythm of the type of movement they describe and accompany. This is a good clue to follow in collecting vocal samples from your group. Turn the children loose in rhythmic movement and then begin from that point. While some continue in movement, others might enjoy sitting down and trying to fit words into the rhythm pattern that is being set by the moving group. Nonsense syllables and sounds like clicking are sometimes an easy beginning to fill in the time between words. Alteration of an already made verse is an easy step for beginners. For example, take the first verse in the walking group and change the repeated word.

The verse is:

> Hear the beat, beat, beat
> Of the feet, feet, feet
> Of the children as they walk
> In the street, street, street.
> —Marguerite Schuberth

A slight change of wording makes the verse read:

> Hear the boom, boom, boom
> And the boom, boom, boom
> Of the children as they walk
> In the room, room, room.
> —First Grader

Walking

A good walking movement is easy and swinging, not stiff and jerky. The body is held straight and the head high. The weight is centered well forward over the advancing foot at all times. Two variations of this are the relaxed walk with body bounding downward at each step and arms swinging to the floor, and the prancy walk with the body arched backward and the knees raised high at each step.

Chants for Walking

Hear the beat, beat, beat
Of the feet, feet, feet
Of the children as they walk
In the street, street, street.
　　　　　—Marguerite Schuberth

Three funny old men from our town
Went out for a walk one day,
The wind blew so hard
That it turned them around,
And they walked the other way,
Yes, they walked the other way.
　　　　　—Nursery Rhyme

Sonata, Op. 14, No. 2

Slow walk

Beethoven

Walking Song

Adapted

German Folk Song

1. As we go walk - ing two by two, Two by two, two by two,
2. Oh, don't you hear the mu - sic play, Mu - sic play, mu - sic play,

Keep step with me, I'll step with you, Two by two.
Oh, don't you hear the mu - sic play, On our way?

Tin Soldiers

J. Wolverton

J. Wolverton

A - rat - a - tat - tat - tat - tat, The lit - tle tin sol - diers come;

(112)

A - rat - a - tat - tat, A - rat - a - tat - tat, I hear the beat of the drum.—

March of the Tin Soldiers

Moderate march time

Tchaikovsky

Theme

Haydn

Soldiers' March

Schumann

Running

Running should be springy and light. The arms should run forward and backward as fast and as hard as the legs are running. Such movement is a goal rather than an accomplishment at the children's ages, as most little children have more of a windmill type of motion than a co-ordinated and balanced drive between arms and legs. The farther forward the body leans in running, the faster the run will be; and the farther backward it leans, the slower the run will be. Running with the arms outstretched at the side or in front of the body will help to develop a feeling of balance in running.

Chants for Running

I like to run, I like to run,
I like to run around.
I like to run, I like to run,
And hear my feet upon the ground.
—Second Grader

We'll follow our leader,
Away we will go,
Away we will go,
Away we will go.
We'll follow our leader,
Away we will go,
Far away, far away we will go.
—Dutch Nursery Rhyme

Badinage

H. Reinhold

The Fair

Cornelius Gurlitt

Gypsy Song

H. Reinhold, Op. 39

The following songs may also be used for running: Take a Little Run About, p. 150, A Rainy Day, p. 39.

Tiptoeing

Tiptoe position high up on the toes is a balance exercise and a good strengthener of the muscles of the feet. When done with a complete body stretch at the same time, it is a compensation for the curved sitting positions children spend their in-school time acquiring. When done in a low half-crouched position, tiptoeing takes on an air of grotesqueness and mystery.

Chants for Tiptoeing

Lightly, lightly tiptoe,
Not a single sound,
Lightly, lightly tiptoe,
Gently move around.

—First Grader

Creepity-creep, creepity-creep.
Shush! Shush! Shush! Shush!
Creepity-creep, creepity-creep,
There's a great big secret to keep!

—Third Grader

A Tiny Man

Translated

Jack-in-the-Pulpit

E. Humperdinck

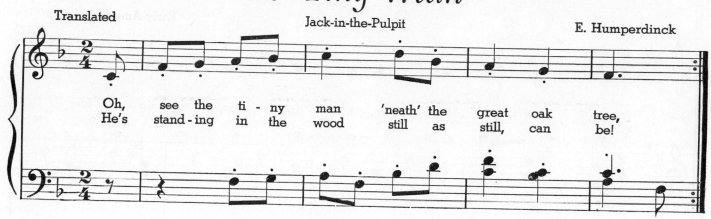

Oh, see the ti - ny man 'neath' the great oak tree,
He's stand - ing in the wood still as still, can be!

Pur - ple coat and cap of red Perched a - top his lit - tle head!

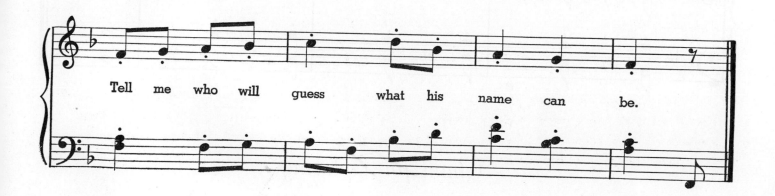

Tell me who will guess what his name can be.

Betty Martin

Early American Song

Hey, Bet - ty Mar - tin, tip - toe, tip - toe;

Hey, Bet - ty Mar - tin, tip - toe fine.

Chant for Tiptoeing

Tip, tip, tippity toe,
Round the room we softly go;
Tip, tip, tippity tee,
There's a secret, come and see;
Tip, tip, tippity tay,
Here's a game we like to play;
Tip, tip, tippity top,
When our heels go down, we stop.

Hall of the Mountain King

Grieg

Jumping

Good jumps will have enough push from the floor to go high or wide in the air and enough flexibility in the feet, ankles, and knees to land without jar or noise. Good landings can be practiced before the jumping is stressed. Standing on steps or low benches and jumping to the floor with complete flexion of all the joints is one way of practicing. The children have called these "Kitty Jumps" because we mentioned that a kitty could jump and never be heard when it landed.

Chants for Jumping

High-jumping is fun,
High-jumping is fun,
High-jumping is fun
For everyone.
　　　　—First Grader

Jack be nimble,
Jack be quick,
Jack jump over
The candlestick.
　　　　—Nursery Rhyme

Jump, Jump

Nina Dawson

C. Reinecke

Jump, jump, Stamp, stamp, stamp, Fol - low in a cir - cle,

Jump, jump, Stamp, stamp, stamp, Fol - low in a cir - cle.

Formation: a circle. The children move in one direction.

Bagatelle

Beethoven, Op. 33

The Strange Man

Schumann, Op. 68

Leap for Life

Cornelius Gurlitt

The following songs may also be used for jumping: The Toad, p. 82, They Ran All About, p. 86.

Hopping

Hopping is continuous movement on the same foot (or on both feet if they are held together and used as one). The free leg may follow in back of the movement or be out in front leading it in any direction. The length of time a child can continue moving on one foot alone can be gradually increased with practice.

Chants for Hopping

Hop, hop, hop!
Hop, hop, hop!
Turn to the right and
Turn to the left and
Change your feet with a
Hop, hop, hop!
    —Second Grader

Handy-Spandy, Jacky-Dandy
Loves plum cake and sugar candy.
He bought some at the grocer's shop
And then away went hop, hop, hop.
    —Nursery Rhyme

The Rabbit

J. W. Beattie

J. W. Beattie

Hop! hop! hop! lit - tle rab - bit in the wood,

Flop! flop! flop! as a lit - tle rab - bit should.

Ecossaises

Lightly, lively

Beethoven

Galloping

The characteristic thing about a gallop is that one foot remains in front all of the time and that it has a marked unevenness of timing and intensity. The higher the knees are bent upward in action, the more marked the rhythm will become.

Chants for Galloping

To market, to market
To buy a fat pig.
Home again, home again,
Rig-a-jig-jig.

     —Nursery Rhyme

I had a little hobby horse,
His name was Tommy Gray;
His head was made of peas-straw,
His body made of hay;
I saddled him and bridled him,
And rode him up to town;
There came a little puff of wind
And blew him up and down.

     —Nursery Rhyme

Hunting Song

C. Reinecke, Op. 77

The Wild Horseman

My Pony

Norma Gillett

Eleanor Vaught

1. My po-ny can gal-lop and gal-lop all day, A
2. He nos-es my pock-et for sug-ar and bread, A

gal-lop, a gal-lop, a gal-lop;   And   off he goes can-ter-ing,
gal-lop, a gal-lop, a gal-lop;   But some-times I give him a

off and a-way, A gal-lop, a gal-lop, a gal-lop.
car-rot in-stead, A gal-lop, a gal-lop, a gal-lop.

The following songs may also be used for galloping: Fox Came a-Loping, p. 88, Yankee Doodle, p. 153.

Skipping

Most children **begin** with a one-foot skip before the step-hop co-ordination is learned for both feet. If the children take hold of their knees and lift them after the step, the hop part of the skip often will occur naturally. Pairing off an easy skipper with a non-skipper sometimes helps. Naming the two movements out loud as they are done will help also; for example, "Step-hop, step-hop, step-hop."

Chants for Skipping

A-skippity skip and a-skippity skip,
A-hippity hop and a-hoppity hip,
One knee up and one knee down,
We go skipping around and around.

— Third Grader

Oh! It's hippity-hop to bed;
I'd rather stay up instead;
But when Father says "must"
There's nothing but just
Go hippity-hop to bed.

— LeRoy Jackson

Pop Goes the Weasel

American Folk Song

1. A pen-ny for a spool of thread, A pen-ny for a nee-dle,
2. — All a-round the chick-en coop The mon-key chased the wea-sel,

That's the way the mon-ey goes, Pop! goes the wea-sel.

Hippity Hop

Adapted

Danish Folk Tune

A skip and a hop and I sail thro' the air, Hip-pi-ty hip-pi-ty hop!

I lift my knees up ver-y high, I bounce al-most to the sky;

Heigh ho! I'm off with a skip and a hop, Hip-pi-ty hip-pi-ty hop!

A Curious Story

Stephen Heller

Sliding

Sliding, while still uneven in timing and intensity, is a smoothly executed movement with little lift from the floor. To begin sliding to the side, step sideward with one foot and then bring the other foot up beside it to take the weight before repeating the process all over again. As this movement is speeded up, a little lift will occur at the time the weight is changed. Sliding may be done forward and backward as in skating. Both arms swing toward the advancing foot. Sliding is an easy and painless way of learning the beginning co-ordination of skating before trying it over rollers or blades.

Chants for Sliding

With a step and a glide,
We move to the side
And slide and slide
And slide.

—First Grader

My feet are winged with silver skates
So I can fly, and fly, and fly;
And as I stroke to right and left,
The stores and houses pass me by.

—Third Grader

Skating

William Dennis

William Dennis

Skat-ing a-round on the ice, we fly, Glid-ing go, glid-ing go;

Frost-y the weath-er and clear the sky; Skat-ing a-round we go.——

Skaters' Waltz

Vigorously

Emil Waldteufel

Sicilienne

Smoothly and not too fast

Schumann

Roller Skating

J. Wolverton

J. Wolverton

Roll, roll-ing a-long,—— Roll, roll-ing a-long!—— The

wheels are whirl-ing a hap-py song, Roll, roll-ing a-long!——

Chant

Roll my ball around, around,
Through the air and on the ground,
To and fro, high and low,
Toss and catch it on the bound.

Bending, Stretching

To stand well, sit well, or walk well, we must know how to stretch every part of the body. The more we stretch, the straighter the body becomes; the more we bend, the more curved and crooked the body becomes. Familiarity and control of both types of movement will give us the best basis for knowing what position our body is in at any time and the ability to correct its alignment.

Chants for Bending, Stretching

I'm all made of hinges,
And everything bends
From the top of my neck
Way down to the ends.
I'm hinges in front
And I'm hinges in back;
But I have to be hinges
Or else I'd crack.
—Aileen Fisher

I stretch and stretch and find it fun
To reach and try to touch the sun.
I bend and bend to touch the floor
Until the muscles in my legs get sore.
—Second Grader

Morning and Evening

Kunigunde Duncan

Grace V. Wilson

Well accentuated

1. I'll tell you the way that get-ting up goes, Stretch and wink and wig-gle your toes,
2. But this is the way that sleep-y time goes, Yawn and nod and take off your clothes,

Then hop out of bed and put on your clothes, That's the way that get-ting up goes.
Then jump in-to bed and soon you will doze, That's the way that sleep-y time goes.

Trees

Mayme Christenson

Marian McLaughlin

Smoothly

The elm will stretch and stretch so wide, It reach - es out on ev - 'ry side; The pine will stretch and stretch so high, It reach - es up to touch the sky; The wil - low droops and droops so low, Its branch - es sweep the ground be - low.

Prelude

Concone, Op. 37, No. 2

Swinging, Swaying

Swinging is pendular in nature. It may be forward and backward, sideward, or circular in direction. Fill all of the time of the swing evenly with movement, so that you do not get to the end in a hurry and wait to come back again.

Chants for Swinging

Day and night, night and day,
The clock is ticking the time away.
Tick-tock, it's one o'clock;
Tick-tock, it's two o'clock.

—Third Grader

Hickory dickory dock,
The mouse ran up the clock,
The clock struck one,
The mouse ran down,
Hickory dickory dock,
Tick-tock.

—Nursery Rhyme

Swinging High, Swinging Low

Mina Dawson

Marian McLaughlin

Smoothly

Swing-ing high, swing-ing low, Leav-ing the ground, up, up I go;

Swing-ing high, swing-ing low, High as the trees I'm swing-ing.

The Fisherman

S. James

Marian McLaughlin

Learning to Swing

Florence Broad

Florence Broad

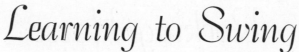

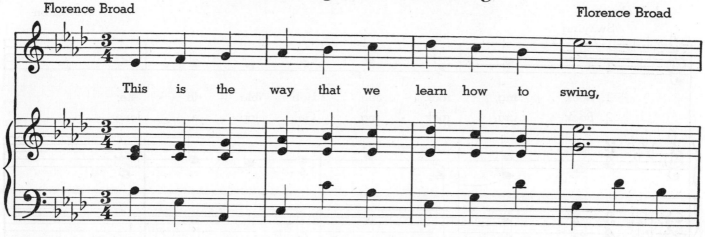

This is the way that we learn how to swing,

Learn how to swing, learn how to swing; This is the way that we

learn how to swing, For - ward and back a - gain.————

The following songs may also be used for swinging: The Cuckoo Clock, p. 164; The Oriole, p. 54.

Rocking Horse

J. Wolverton

J. Wolverton

Swaying

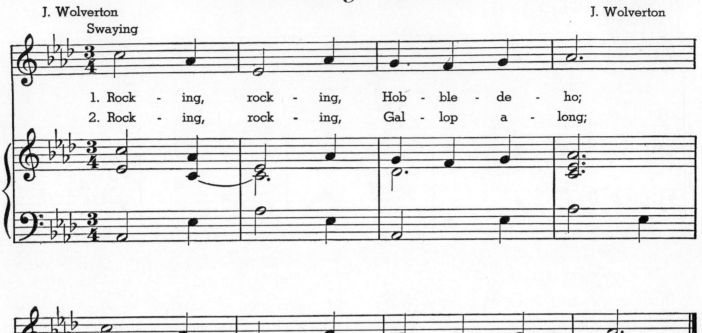

1. Rock - ing, rock - ing, Hob - ble - de - ho;
2. Rock - ing, rock - ing, Gal - lop a - long;

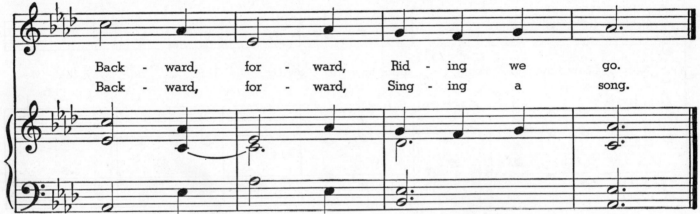

Back - ward, for - ward, Rid - ing we go.
Back - ward, for - ward, Sing - ing a song.

The following songs may also be used for swaying: Lullabies, pp. 4, 6, 12; Autumn, p. 32.

Mountain March

Norwegian Folk Song

Waltz

Brahms

Oh, Where Is My Little Dog Gone?

German Folk Song

Adapted
Moderately

Oh, where, oh, where is my lit-tle dog gone?

Oh, where, oh, where—is he?———— With his tail so short and his

ears so long, Oh, where, oh, where can he be?————

The Blue Danube Waltz

Johann Strauss

Turning, Twisting

Turning is exciting movement, emotionally and physically. The body can stand only short intervals of it in any one direction without dizziness. A feeling of dizziness can be avoided if the head and body are held straight and unwavering as an axis for the turning, or if the direction of the turn is reversed frequently. Both arms wind up around the body in preparation for a good swing and continue to wind up for a turn in the reverse direction when the turning movement is stopped. Sometimes turning proceeds from one level to another like a spiral staircase. When one part of the body gets ahead of the other parts it is called "twisting movement."

Chants for Turning

Round about
And round about
And round about and round about
And round about
And round about
I go.
—A. A. Milne

(Each of these lines is said in the same length of time to give the turn great acceleration and then retard it.)

Like a leaf or feather
In the windy weather,
We will whirl about and twirl about
And then sink down together.
—Marguerite Schuberth

Tarantella

Mendelssohn, Op. 102, No. 3

Change direction of turn or twist on each phrase.

The Dancing Dolly

Mayme Christenson

J. W. Beattie

Waltz time, lightly

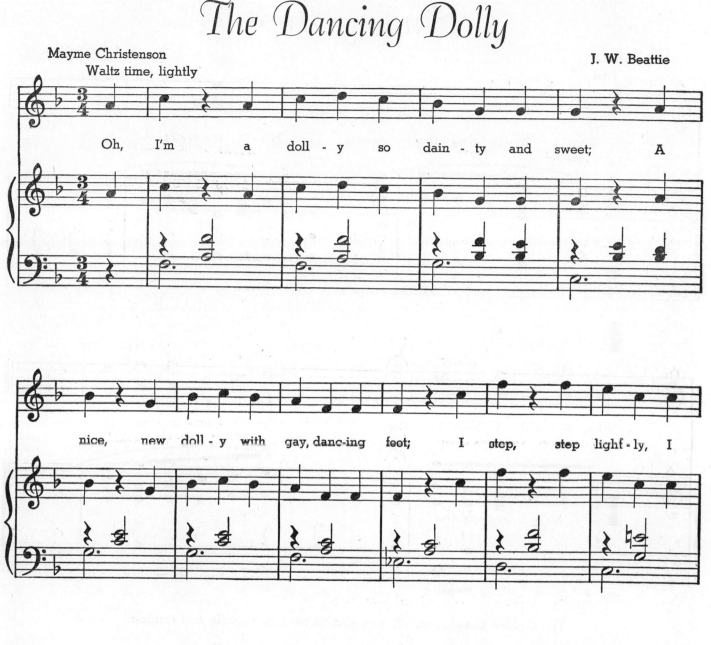

Oh, I'm a doll - y so dain - ty and sweet; A

nice, new doll - y with gay, danc-ing feet; I step, step light - ly, I

step, step bright - ly, I turn and step with my gay, danc-ing feet.

Singing Top

J. Wolverton

J. Wolverton

I'm a lit-tle sing-ing top,   Hm-m-m-m-m-m-m;

When I'm tired I have to stop,   Hm-m-m-m-m-m-m.

"The Golden Leaves," p. 35, may also be used for twisting and turning.

Dancing Doll

E. Poldini

⊙ Change direction of turn or twist.

Reaper's Song

Schumann, Op. 68

⊙ Change direction of turn or twist.

RHYTHMIC VARIATIONS
Take a Little Run About

J. Wolverton

H. Hinga

Take a lit - tle run a - bout, Oh, take a lit - tle run a - bout,

Take a lit - tle run a - bout, And then come home.

Variations
Skip

Take a lit - tle skip a - bout, etc.

Hop, jump

Take a lit - tle hop a - bout, etc.

Walk

Take a lit - tle walk a - bout, etc.

Sway

Take a lit - tle slide a - bout, etc.

Jing Jang

American Folk Song

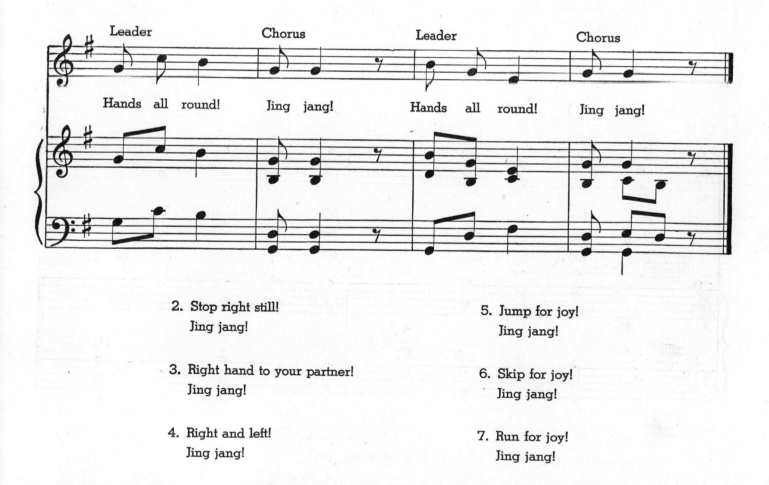

2. Stop right still!
   Jing jang!

3. Right hand to your partner!
   Jing jang!

4. Right and left!
   Jing jang!

5. Jump for joy!
   Jing jang!

6. Skip for joy!
   Jing jang!

7. Run for joy!
   Jing jang!

This number may be used as a simple action song. Stanzas 3 and 4, which suggest rather difficult movements (play-party type), may be omitted.

Hey Jim Along, Jim Along Josie

American Folk Song

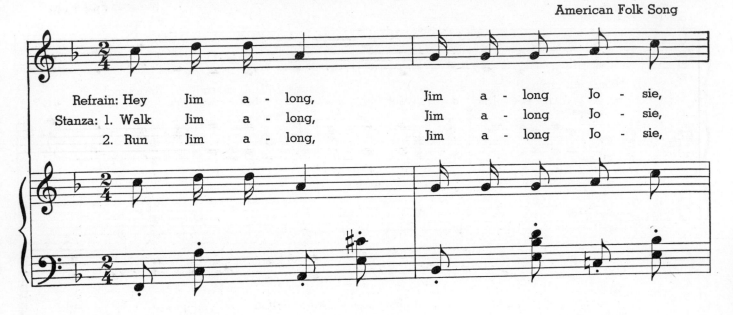

Refrain: Hey Jim a - long,   Jim a - long Jo - sie,
Stanza: 1. Walk Jim a - long,   Jim a - long Jo - sie,
      2. Run Jim a - long,   Jim a - long Jo - sie,

Hey Jim a - long,   Jim a - long Jo.
Walk Jim a - long,   Jim a - long Jo.
Run Jim a - long,   Jim a - long Jo.

3. Hop Jim along, etc.

4. Tiptoe along, etc.

Yankee Doodle

Traditional

Old Tune

(1) — Yan - kee Doo - dle went to town, — Rid - ing on a po - ny,

— Stuck a feath - er in his cap And called it mac - a - ro - ni!

(1) Trotting Ponies

(2) Prancing (stepping high)

(3) Galloping

(4) Tired Horses

(153)

Jingle Bells

Fast

J. Pierpont

Jin - gle bells,   jin - gle bells,   Jin - gle all the way,

Oh, what fun it is to ride in a one - horse o - pen sleigh—   one - horse o - pen sleigh!

Play the song in these variations (skipping, galloping, jumping, hopping).

etc.

Walk

etc.

Recorded Material

Listening to recorded music should not be an isolated experience but should grow out of needs and activities related to the daily music program. Listening to records has little value unless it is related to the child's experience or is something he can comprehend and make his own. But carefully chosen records are of distinct value for rhythmic response and for quiet listening.

Records for Rhythm*

WALKING
March, "Alceste." Gluck
March of the Toys. Victor Herbert
Minuet, "Don Giovanni." Mozart

RUNNING
Badinage. Victor Herbert
Scherzo, "Midsummer Night's Dream." Mendelssohn
Run, Run, Run. Concone
Tarantella. Saint-Saëns

TIPTOEING
Minuet. Paderewski
Pizzicati. Delibes
Amaryllis. Ghys

HOPPING
Entrance of the Little Fauns. Pierné
Johnny at the Fair. English Folk Dance
Highland Schottische. Scottish Folk Dance
L'Arabesque. Burgmüller

JUMPING
Dance of the Clowns, "Midsummer Night's Dream." Mendelssohn
Dance of the Tumblers, "Snow Maiden." Rimsky-Korsakov

SKIPPING
Giga. Corelli
Elfin Dance. Jensen, Op. 33, No. 5
Gathering Peascods. English Folk Dance

GALLOPING
Postillion. Godard, Op. 55, No. 1
Light Cavalry Overture. Suppé
The Little Hunters. Kullak

SLIDING
Czarina. Gann
Skating. Kullak
Lott' ist Tod. Swedish Folk Dance

STRETCHING AND BENDING
Country Dance. Weber
Lullabies and Work Songs
Waltz No. 2. Brahms

SWINGING AND SWAYING
Walzer. Gurlitt
Waltzes 1, 2, 9. Brahms, Op. 39
Valse. Poldini

TURNING AND TWISTING
March of the Dwarfs. Grieg
Spinning Song. Mendelssohn
The Music Box. Liadow

BEATING AND SHAKING
Dance Song. Omaha Dance
Butterfly Dance. Hopi Dance
Shuffling Feet. Sioux Dance

Quiet Listening

There are occasions when children enjoy quiet listening. The use of recorded music for quiet listening, however, often results in experiences that are of little value to the child. The material must be simple, definite in character, and easily comprehended by the children. The span of attention is short; therefore, the time devoted to this experience must be brief and to the point. Quiet, passive listening requires music of contrasting types. A lullaby (sleepy music), a toy soldiers' march, a tiptoe dance might give the variety that would help to hold interest and attention in this kind of listening.

Records for Quiet Listening*

Air de Ballet. Jadassohn
The Bee. Schubert
Clowns, "Midsummer Night's Dream." Mendelssohn
Cradle Song. Schubert
The Dwarfs. Reinhold
Elfin Dance. Grieg
Fairies (Scherzo). Schubert
The Gnomes. Reinhold
Humoresque. Dvořák
The Little Sandman. Brahms
Lullaby. Brahms
Lullaby. Mozart
Mirror Dance, "Faust Ballet." Gounod
Of a Tailor and a Bear. MacDowell
Sweet and Low. Barnby
To a Water Lily. MacDowell
To a Wild Rose. MacDowell

*These are Victor recordings and can be found in the Victor catalogue.

Toy Instruments

Percussion instruments offer the children an opportunity to hear and produce a much wider range of musical sound than the voice can produce. It is the first instrumental experience most children of this age have, and therefore the greatest care should be taken in selecting instruments which have good qualities of tone. Cheap, tinny-sounding cymbals, drums that are flat and toneless, and unresonant rhythm sticks are a poor investment at any price, if the building of good musical taste is considered.

Instruments which sound well are not necessarily expensive; in fact, the clever teacher will be able to assemble without any cost instruments of each type commonly used. The cheapest "Rhythm Band Outfit" listed by commercial houses costs $5.45. Here is a comparison of a commercial and a homemade set:

Commercial Rhythm Band Outfit
Cost: $5.45

8 pairs of rhythm sticks
(made from unresonant ⅜ inch dowling)

2 jingle clogs
(small wooden paddle with a metal disk on one end)

2 sleigh bells
(three small bells on a strip of webbing)

2 cymbals with strap and beater

1 triangle with beater

1 tone block and beater

Homemade Rhythm Instruments
Cost: Nothing

8 pairs of rhythm sticks
(made from old broomsticks which are solid and resonant)

2 jingle clogs
(made from tongue depresser with a roofing disk at one end)

2 sleigh bells
(either a 10-cent card of 12 Christmas bells sewed on cloth, or metal bottle caps with a hole nailed through and sewed to a strip of cloth)

2 cymbals with beater
(the covers from cast aluminum cooking utensils are resonant, as are brass trays. Pencils make good beaters.)

1 triangle
(bars of metal which have been curtain rods or plant supports are often resonant. They can be bent into triangular shape.)

1 tone block and beater
(an old bowling pin or baseball bat can be sectioned and grooved to sound like wood block.)

However, a much better selection of instruments for primary use can be made by the teacher if she is allowed a small amount of money for the purpose. The selection may be made to have examples from each of the four main groupings of the percussion family as it is found in real orchestras. These sections are the resonant metals, the resonant woods, the drums, and the rattles. Some examples of each kind are given on the next page, with homemade substitutes in parentheses:

Resonant Metals

Gongs (old brake bands)
Cymbals (brass ash trays)
Triangles (curtain rods)
Chimes (curtain rods)

Resonant Woods

Xylophones (red-wood strips)
Wood blocks (baseball-bat sections)
Temple blocks (bowling-pin sections)
Claves (paired sticks)

Drums

Kettle drum (chopping bowl with calfskin head thumbtacked over it)
Tom-tom (wooden keg, metal can, or cardboard carton with laced-on or nailed-on drum head of old inner tubes or calfskin)
Snare drum (same as the above, with coiled wire stretched across one end)
Bass drum (waste basket of the solid type or a lard can or soft-drink barrel with laced-on or nailed-on drum head)

Rattles

Strip rattles (bottle tops, beads, nuts, or shells tied on cloth or on strips of leather tied around the ankles or arms)

Stick rattles (strips like the above tied on handles)

Container rattles (gourds with the seeds dried in them, or paired oyster shells with a bit of gravel sealed inside, or cardboard cans of small size with chalk or gravel sealed inside)

Container rattles on sticks (any of the above mounted on handles)

With a percussion orchestra representing each of these four types of sound, the children can provide accompaniment for any of their rhythmic movement and singing needs. Small groups of children may play while others are moving, or large groups may play while a few are moving. The sharper- and shorter-sounding instruments are best for the quicker and more percussive types of movement, while the longer-lasting sounds of the metal instruments are better for movements which stretch over a longer time interval.

Creative Rhythm

Free Response

Dramatized or "pretending" rhythms have a place in the music program. However, to restrict the rhythmic activities to those in which children pretend they are brownies, fairies, falling leaves, toy soldiers, windmills, or animals of various kinds is to place limitations on what may be more truly creative. There is no challenge to the child, and his development is thwarted if he hears the same music every day, performed in the same way, and responds to it with the same bodily movements. The imaginative teacher will provide, by means of piano or phonograph, the opportunity for children to hear and respond to many kinds of music. She will present music with variety in tempo, dynamics, meter, and mood. She will often ask such questions as: "Is the music soft or loud, slow or fast, smooth or jerky, big or little?" If the music played was slow and soft and a child replied that it was fast and loud, the teacher asks the class to listen once more, for unlimited freedom of response without guidance or thought often ends in confusion.

The creative teacher encourages children to interpret the music by appropriate bodily movement. She will often say something like this: "John, you had an excellent idea then. Will you show it to the class?" Or: "Mary, did you see someone move in a way which you especially liked?"

To secure freedom of response, it is often helpful to call attention to the various hinges of the body which allow movement: neck, shoulders, elbows, wrists, fingers, waist, hips, knees, ankles, and feet. While she cannot be too technical, the teacher may give such a direction as: "Let your heads do something as this music is played." Or: "This time, use your arms, knees, and heads." Such suggestions often result in great variety of rhythm responses, and the opportunity to respond freely affords the type of challenge which stimulates growth.

Pattern Making

Children can create and produce musical ideas in such a way as to become familiar with certain fundamentals of music, the naming of which may be left to later years. Thus, sounds that are slow or fast later take on definite time values; a pattern becomes a musical motive; a phrase repeated becomes a musical phrase. With little children all that is important is the response, not the name.

To bring about response, the teacher may ask for a specific type of pattern. "Who can clap a pattern that says fast?" The response may be clapped or played on a drum, rhythm stick, or any percussive instrument. "Now a slow pattern." "Now both fast and slow." Allow the child to experiment enough times until some definite succession of sounds or patterns has been formulated. He can then repeat it many times alone or with other children, using instruments, clapping, stepping, or in bodily movement. A series of patterns might result, each played at least three times:

Fast, fast, fast, fast
Slow, slow
Fast, fast, fast, fast, slow, slow
Slow, slow, fast, fast, fast, fast
Soft, soft, soft, loud, loud, loud
Soft, loud, soft, loud
Soft, soft, soft, soft, loud

Other suggestions might include:
Clap a pattern that walks.
Clap a pattern that runs.
Walk and run in the same pattern.
Let's have one that skips.

Now one that gallops.
Whose name sounds like a walking pattern?
(John Ward, John Ward, John Ward)
Whose name sounds like a run?
(Mary Walker, Mary Walker, Mary Walker)
Whose name has both a walk and a run?
(Frank Cooper, Frank Cooper, Frank Cooper)
Give us one with a run and a walk.
(Georgie Clay, Georgie Clay, Georgie Clay)
Whose name gallops?
(Marie McCall, Marie McCall, Marie McCall)

Children will express themselves in the same way by chanting names of different fruits and vegetables. The more of such devices the teacher uses, the more alert children will be in their responses.

Always keep in mind: Rhythm must be felt and given some form of bodily movement.

To summarize, help children in the following ways:

1. Develop variety in rhythmic reponse by
   a. changing tempo
      slow—fast
   b. changing dynamics
      loud—soft
   c. changing direction
      forward—backward
      circle left—circle right
      stand in place.

2. Encourage creativeness and originality.

3. Develop good movement in basic rhythms such as walking and running, and help children to recognize, feel, name, and give expression to these rhythms.

Shaking and Beating

Beating is a shaking movement which contacts a drum or the floor or some part of the body to make a sound with each movement. Shaking movements are usually smaller and may or may not be done with rattles of the strip or handle variety.

Chants for Shaking and Beating

Shake your rattles high
Shake your rattles low
Shake your rattles to the side
As around you go.
   —Kindergarteners

Beat, beat, beat, beat!
Beat upon the tom-tom.
Beat, beat, beat, beat!
Beat upon the drum.
   —Lew Sarett

Indian Dance

RATTLES
J. W. Beattie

My Drum

Adapted

DRUMS

Folk Tune

I have a lit-tle drum, I hold it in my hand,

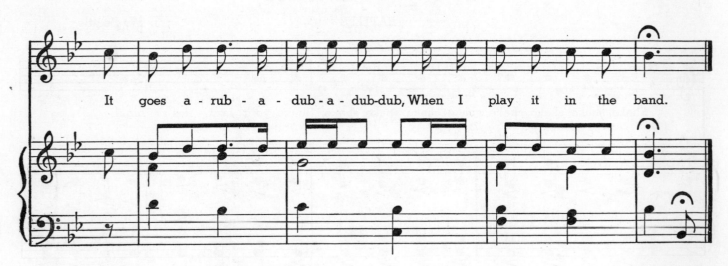

It goes a-rub-a-dub-a-dub-dub, When I play it in the band.

My Rhythm Sticks

J. Wolverton

RHYTHM STICKS

J. Wolverton

My rhy-thm sticks go click-click-clack With a click! (x x) And a clack (x x)

My rhy-thm sticks go click-click-clack With a click! (x x) And a clack! (x x)

The Cymbals

Elizabeth Waterman   CYMBALS   Mina Dawson

Fast

Crash! zing! the cym-bals sing, A-round and a-round I go.

Cymbal crash

Cymbal roll

Reverse direction

Crash! zing! the cym-bals sing, Slow-er, slow-er, slow.

Cymbal crash

Cymbal roll

A cymbal roll is made by holding two cymbals together and rubbing them in opposite directions.

The Eskimo Hunter

RATTLES AND DRUMS

Adapted

Eskimo Folk Song

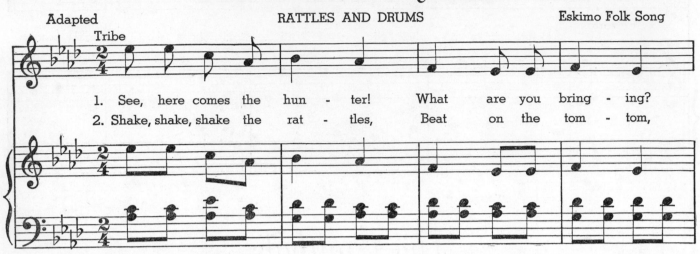

1. See, here comes the hun - ter! What are you bring - ing?
2. Shake, shake, shake the rat - tles, Beat on the tom - tom,

Seals I am bring - ing, Fish I am bring - ing.
Beat on the tom - tom, Beat on the tom - tom.

We'll have meat and will be warm When cold winds blow.
Shake, shake, shake, and beat, beat, beat The hunt - ing song.

The Navajo

J. Wolverton   DRUMS   J. Wolverton

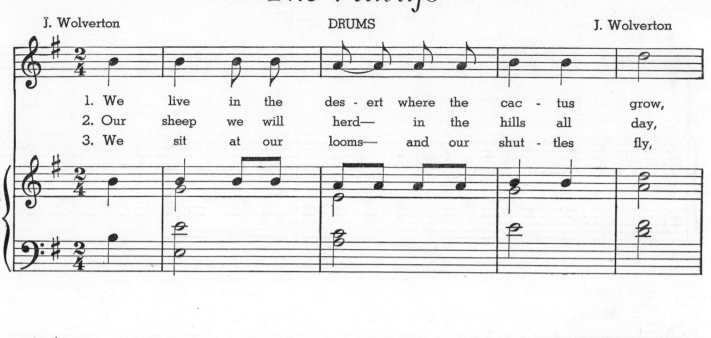

1. We live in the des - ert where the cac - tus grow,
2. Our sheep we will herd— in the hills all day,
3. We sit at our looms— and our shut - tles fly,

We are the chil - dren of the Nav - a - jo;
They give us wool— for our blan - kets gay;
Weav - ing the rugs— for— you to buy;

Yo ho ho, Yo ho ho!

(163)

The Cuckoo Clock

Timothy Fetler RHYTHM STICKS Timothy Fetler

I can tell the time of day By the little clock up - on the wall; Ev - 'ry hour it ticks a - way, Then I hear a fun - ny lit - tle call:

Cuck - oo, Cuck - oo, Then I hear a fun-ny lit - tle call.

Play a tick-tock sound throughout with rhythm sticks.

My Tambourine

TAMBOURINE

J. Wolverton

J. Wolverton

1. Lis - ten to my tam - bour - ine! Ting - a - ling-ling, Ting - a - ling - ling!
2. Lis - ten to my tam - bour - ine! Tap - a - tap-tap, Tap - a - tap - tap!
3. Lis - ten to my tam - bour - ine! Ting - a - ling-ling, Tap - a - tap - tap!

Lis - ten to my tam - bour - ine! Ting - a - ling-ling - a ling!——
Lis - ten to my tam - bour - ine! Tap - a - tap-tap - a - tap!——
Lis - ten to my tam - bour - ine! Ting - a - ling, tap - a - tap!——

My Bugle

Adapted   TONETTES OR BLOW INSTRUMENTS   French Folk Tune

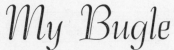
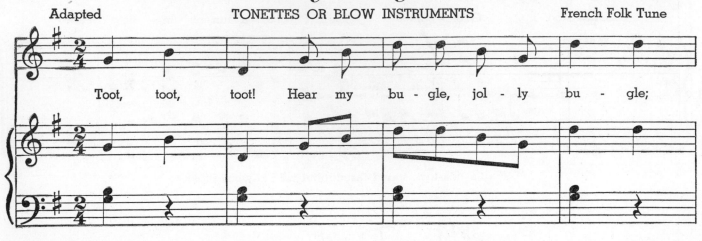

Toot, toot, toot! Hear my bu - gle, jol - ly bu - gle;

Toot, toot, toot! Hear my bu - gle loud and clear.

Little Boy Blue

R. A. Coan   TONETTES OR BLOW INSTRUMENTS   R. A. Coan

Gaily

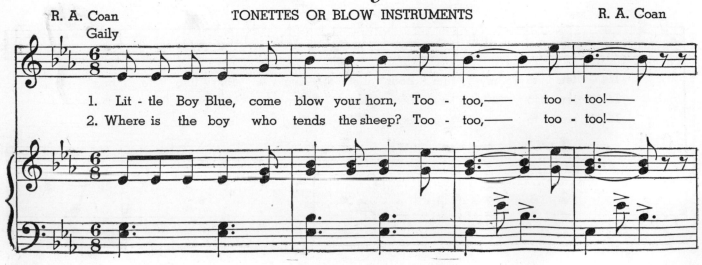

1. Lit - tle Boy Blue, come blow your horn, Too - too,——— too - too!———
2. Where is the boy who tends the sheep? Too - too,——— too - too!———

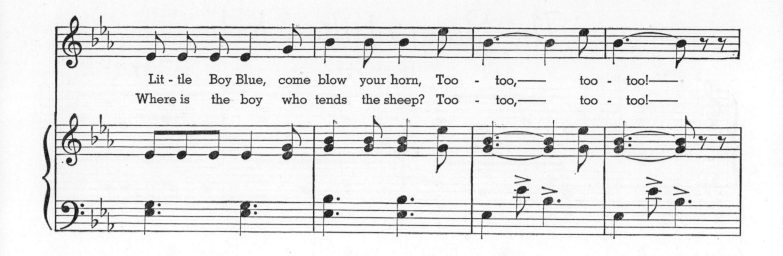

Lit - tle Boy Blue, come blow your horn, Too - too,—— too - too!
Where is the boy who tends the sheep? Too - too,—— too - too!——

Lit - tle Boy Blue, come blow your horn, The sheep's in the mead-ow, the cow's in the corn.
Where is the boy who tends the sheep? He's un - der the hay - cock fast a -sleep.

Too - too, too-too, too - too,—— too-too, too - too, too - too!——
Too - too, too-too, too - too,—— too-too, too - too, too - too!——

The Song of the Clock

WOOD BLOCKS

Theodore Kullak

My Triangle

TRIANGLES

S. James

S. James

I love to hear the tri-an-gle ring, Ring, ding!— — Ring, ding!— — — A mer-ry tune it likes— to sing, Ring, ding!— — — Ring, ding!— — —

Tunes for Toy Instruments

Small xylophones, both wooden and metal, are quite commonly used in the home and at school. These instruments range in tone from eight wooden or metal bars to twelve. Most of the instruments are tuned to the Key of C, although it is possible to play in the Key of G by omitting songs which contain F#.

A certain amount of aid should be given the child to help him identify certain tones. If the instrument is in the Key of C, these tones are C, E, G, C'; in the Key of G the tones most often used are G, B, D, G'.

The following suggestions are given:

a. Take a piece of tag board or heavy paper. Cut an oblong piece the length of the instrument. Cut it wide enough so that when folded lengthwise, it will stand up alone behind the instrument.

b. Draw in each block or bar, using vertical lines. Make these lines in the exact position of the bars on the instrument. On this upright card there should be as many blocks as there are blocks on the instrument.

c. Color the first block on the card RED. This identifies the tone C. Color the third YELLOW (E), the fifth GREEN (G), the eighth BLUE (C).

When playing in the Key of G, the card is shifted so that the red color is behind G; the yellow, behind B; the green, behind D; and the blue, behind G.

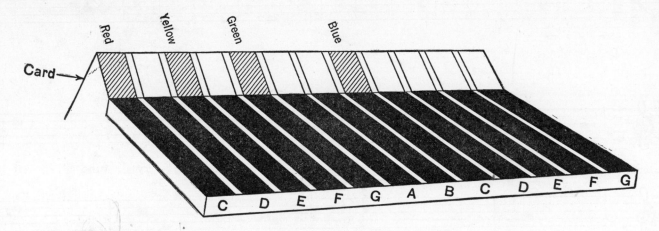

Icicles

Grace V. Wilson

Key of C (can be played in G)

I - ci - cles high, Drip, drip, drip, drip, drip, drip, drop!

Bells

Ding, dong, ding, dong! Four o'-clock the chimes are ring-ing;

Back and forth the bells are swing-ing, Ding, dong, ding, dong!

Apples

Ap - ples, ap - ples in the tree, Some are high, Some are low.

The Train

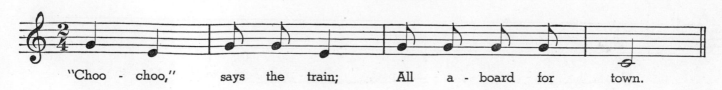

"Choo - choo," says the train; All a - board for town.

The Clock

Key of G (can be played in C)

Tick - tock,　Tick - tock,　Goes the lit - tle clock.

Time for School

Come　to　school,　It's　nine　o' - clock.

The Kitten

"Me - ow!　Me - ow!"　Hear　the　kit - ten　call.

Auto Horns

"Honk! Honk! Honk!　Honk! Honk! Honk!"　Au - to　horns　are　call - ing.

The Engine

I'm　the　en - gine　puff - ing past,　Puff - puff! Toot - toot!　Go - ing　fast.

Topical Index — Rote Songs

Topical Index — Rhythmic Movements

Alphabetical Index